CROSSBOW and OVERCAST

# CROSSBOW AND

William Morrow & Co., Inc., 1964

# OVERCAST

New York                    JAMES McGOVERN

**BY THE SAME AUTHOR**

*Fräulein*
*No Ruined Castles*
*The Berlin Couriers*

TO W. Clement Stone

# Contents

PART THREE: **AFTERMATH**

# Illustrations

Following page 120

*V-2 Rocket in flight.*

*Hermann Oberth and Wernher von Braun, Berlin, August 1930.*

*Heinrich Himmler at Peenemünde.*

*Test firing of the V-2.*

*Aerial reconnaissance photograph of rocket Test Stand VII, Peenemünde.*

*V-1 component stores on the French coast.*

*V-1 captured intact.*

*Entrance to tunnel of the Mittelwerke.*

*Partially completed V-2's in the Mittelwerke.*

*Dornberger and von Braun, May 1945.*

*Major Robert Staver, Fleischer, and Riedel with captured V-2 documents.*

*Major Hamill, Colonel Toftoy, and Wernher von Braun at Fort Bliss.*

*Colonel Hamill, von Braun, and Major General Toftoy at a re-union, 1958.*

*Wernher von Braun and Dr. Kurt Debus in front of the Saturn rocket.*

# PART ONE
# CROSSBOW

DENMARK

PEENEMÜNDE

HAMBURG
CUXHAVEN
Weser River
Elbe River
STETTIN
POLAND
EBERSWALDE
BERLIN
NETHERLANDS
HILDESHEIM
WEST GERMANY
MAGDEBURG
GOSLAR
EAST GERMANY
KASSEL
NORDHAUSEN
BLEICHERODE
LEIPZIG
COLOGNE
Rhine River
BELGIUM
FULDA
DRESDEN
Neisse River
Oder River
LUXEM-BOURG
FRANKFURT
PRAGUE
CZECHOSLOVAKIA
NUREMBERG
STUTTGART
Danube River
FRANCE
LANDSHUT
MUNICH
OBERAMMERGAU
Oberjoch Pass
HINDELANG
GARMISCH-PARTENKIRCHEN
SONTHOFEN
AUSTRIA
REUTTE
INNSBRUCK
SWITZERLAND
ITALY

●●●●● AREA ADVANCED TO BY THE WESTERN ALLIES
AS OF V-E DAY, MAY 8, 1945

▬▬▬▬ AREA WITHDRAWN TO BY THE WESTERN ALLIES
BEGINNING JULY 1, 1945, CONSTITUTING
PRESENT BORDER BETWEEN EAST AND WEST
GERMANY AND BETWEEN WEST GERMANY AND
CZECHOSLOVAKIA

# 1

## Something queer

As night fell, the village turned silent and dark. Its name was
Dörnten. For centuries it had been a tiny and insignificant
mining community resting on the northern edge of the Harz,
the mountain range that rises abruptly from the flat plain of
central Germany.

It was April 4, 1945. American combat units were thirty
miles from the Harz Mountains and relentlessly advancing on
them. But Dörnten remained in German hands, and a strict
curfew and blackout were in effect in the village. All of its
lights had been turned off, the windows of its houses were
shuttered, and its streets were empty of people and traffic.

Then, shortly after nightfall, the silence was broken. A
single truck rumbled over the cobblestones of Dörnten's
main street. With its headlights switched off, the vehicle
moved slowly by moonlight to a mine just outside the village.

Had anyone been watching the shadowy occupants of the
truck, he might have wondered why they had driven to this
particular mine. It was of no military importance. It had, in
fact, been abandoned five years earlier because of the low
quality of its ore. Except for an elderly caretaker and his
wife, no one lived in its immediate vicinity. And yet the men

in the truck acted as though they had some urgent, important business to accomplish.

The vehicle was parked before an open tunnel that ran deep into the side of a low hill and was served by a railroad track. Seven German soldiers and two civilian engineers, Bernhard Tessmann and Dieter Huzel, jumped out of the truck. Quickly they began to fulfill the purpose that had brought them to this deserted spot: hiding from the approaching Allies the most valuable documents in the dying Third Reich.

The documents were contained in wooden boxes which were unloaded from the truck, and then from two others which were driven to the mine during the night. Fourteen tons of numbered boxes were eventually loaded onto flatcars on the railroad track at the tunnel's mouth. Then the flatcars were pulled by an electric-battery-operated locomotive a thousand feet into the tunnel, stopping at a gallery which branched off from the track. At the end of the gallery was a small, dry room that had once been a powder magazine.

Struggling and sweating in the damp chill of the mine, the nine Germans unloaded the boxes from the flatcars and hauled them to the small room. It was not until eleven o'clock the next morning—when American dive bombers were streaking over Dörnten—that the last box was in place. The room's iron door was locked. Then the gallery leading to it was hidden from view by rocks and timbers blasted into it by a charge of dynamite.

Tessmann, Huzel, and the seven soldiers drove away from the mine, satisfied that no enemy could ever find this hiding place. The two engineers, however, were the only men in the world who knew both its exact location and the nature of the material that had been hidden. The soldiers had been locked inside the trucks by Huzel and Tessmann, who acted as drivers, on the approach to Dörnten. The same thing was done during the departure, so that the soldiers could not reveal, even if they had wanted to, where the mine was located. The mine caretaker had supplied miners' hats and lamps and acted as a guide for the operation. But he had been told nothing about the material beyond the fact that it was "classified military information."

Actually this "classified military information" was a unique scientific treasure, one that was at that very moment being searched for by all of the Allies. The boxes hidden in the mine contained all of the designs and technical data for "Hitler's Secret Weapon," the world's first long-range rocket, V-2. If Hitler himself had reacted differently to the development of V-2, the entire course of the war might have been changed. As it was, over a thousand V-2's had been fired against England, but they had failed to save Germany from the defeat that was now imminent. To a small circle of Allied technical experts, however, V-2 itself was not a complete failure. It had changed the nature of warfare and left behind a terrifying spectacle of what a future war might be like.

The Third Reich had less than a month to live. British, Soviet, and American intelligence services had already begun a three-way struggle to secure for their own countries the V-2 documents and the rocket experts who had produced them. To the knowledgeable, these spoils of war represented two inevitable future developments: intercontinental ballistic missiles and big booster rockets capable of orbiting men around the earth and later to the moon and perhaps even to the planets beyond.

In the secret, three-way competition whose outcome would affect the fortunes of mankind for generations to come, the British, in May 1945 began with a distinct advantage over their allies, despite the approach of American troops to the Harz Mountain area where the V-2 documents were hidden and where most of the German rocket specialists were living. British Intelligence had good reason to know more about V-2 and the men who had developed the world's first and only long-range rocket than either the Americans or the Soviets.

Huzel, Tessmann, and the soldiers who had helped them drove away from Dörnten into a chaotic Germany verging on total defeat. But two years earlier, because of certain disquieting information received by the British Government at the very time when Allied victory could at last be foreseen, that defeat had suddenly appeared to be far from inevitable. An investigation had been ordered which grew into the most intensive secret intelligence operation of all time. This operation would end with the capture, by one of the Allies, of the leading V-2 experts and the cache of scientific information hidden behind the dynamited gallery of the Dörnten mine. It began with Duncan Sandys.

Duncan Sandys, a tall, broad-shouldered man with wavy red hair and a pleasant smile, looked like the very model of a rising young Conservative Party politician. He walked with "a distinguished limp" and was married to Winston Churchill's daughter Diana.

In mid-April 1943, at the age of thirty-four, Sandys was given the first in a series of difficult assignments, the solution to which would bring him to high posts* in the British Government. The British Chiefs of Staff had become concerned with persistent reports of German experiments with secret weapons and recommended to Winston Churchill that Sandys be appointed to investigate them. After a month of "enthralling speculation," Sandys prepared to submit his first report to the War Cabinet.

It would not be comforting, but Sandys hoped that it would cause the Cabinet to share his concern and act upon it. The Allied leaders were not complacent, but they could

* Sandys later became Minister of Aviation and Minister of Defence. As of June 1964, he was Secretary for Colonial and Commonwealth Affairs.

be excused for their belief that victory was in sight. The Germans had lost North Africa, Stalingrad, control of the air, and Sicily would soon be invaded. But Sandys believed that his investigation, granted that it had the implausible overtones of the most bizarre kind of spy fiction, had revealed the existence of German weapons which could reverse, in a sudden and terrifying way, the trend of Allied victory.

Sandys had first pondered the mysterious Oslo Letters,* which had reached British Intelligence from Norway in November 1939. They were anonymous but undoubtedly came from a high German government official who was a member of the anti-Nazi underground. They contained detailed reports of secret German development of a variety of new weapons, among them an account of experimental work with long-range rockets on an isolated island off the Baltic coast. The Oslo Letters had something of a Jules Verne ring to them. They were filed for future reference, but, beyond that, nothing had been done about them.

Sandys then considered some photographs that had been taken by Flight Lieutenant D. W. Steventon of the Photographic Reconnaissance Unit on May 15, 1942. Steventon had flown his Spitfire high over the western Baltic to photograph German destroyers berthed at Swinemünde. Having done this, he passed over the nearby village of Peenemünde** on the northern tip of the wooded, isolated island of Usedom and chanced to see a new airfield there. He had some film left and switched on his cameras. Back in England, photo

---

* The Oslo Letters were sent to the British Naval Attaché in Oslo by an anonymous correspondent. If the British Government ever learned his identity, it has never made it public. As the war went on, one development after another described in the letters actually appeared. Dr. R. V. Jones, Chief of the Scientific Intelligence Branch of the Air Ministry, remarked: ". . . in the few dull moments of the War I used to look up the Oslo Report to see what should be coming along next."

** Pronounced Pay' • neh • min'deh (Pā'nē • mün'dē).

interpreters found that the new airfield was surrounded by circular embankments and other oddly shaped buildings. As with the Oslo Letters, nothing had been done with these photographs beyond filing them. But now Sandys directed more intensive photographic coverage of Usedom to be made.

He next went through certain intelligence reports that had been arriving with disquieting frequency in the past six months from Denmark, Sweden, Norway, and Poland. They were sketchy, in most cases only reports of rumors, but they did form a pattern. Danish Intelligence, for example, reported that fishermen had seen strange objects with "flaming tails" streaking across the night sky as they fished off the Danish island of Bornholm; the objects seemed to come from Peenemünde on the nearby German island of Usedom.

More solid news came from Polish Home Army Intelligence, which reported that the Germans had definitely constructed a unique research installation at Peenemünde. Polish slave laborers had been recruited for work there and were housed at Trassenheide, a settlement for foreign workers on Usedom Island. In fact, two members of the Polish Underground with technical training had chanced to be among those Poles sent to Trassenheide by the Germans. They had been permitted to enter the heavily guarded secret part of the installation on a brief tour of latrine duty. One of them had passed a shed with its door ajar. Inside he spotted a torpedo-shaped object with wings. It looked like a midget airplane and yet it had no cockpit or any other space for a pilot. This news and a crude layout of the Peenemünde installation were duly passed on to London by the Polish Underground.

All the available evidence about a new secret weapon pointed to Peenemünde, Sandys thought. It was a secluded spot which down through the centuries had never been anything more than a tiny fishing village, a poor relation to the fashionable seaside resorts strung out like pearls along the Baltic coast. The ideal solution to the mystery of what was going on there would be to infiltrate a few agents with scientific training inside the place. But this proved to be beyond even the resources of the British Secret Intelligence Service with its effective network of spies all over the continent. As the war turned against Germany, the SS had stepped up its police-state measures and thrown an impenetrable cordon around Peenemünde. Still, even this was a clue. Such extreme security precautions would hardly be taken to close off another routine experimental station.

Something definitely peculiar was going on at Peenemünde, Sandys became convinced, but just exactly what? He had the German radio monitored, and this yielded increasing boasts of new "miracle weapons" that would win the war for Germany. There were no specifics about these *Wunderwaffen*, and the campaign could be dismissed as a propaganda ploy to bolster civilian morale shaken by Stalingrad and the aerial bombardment of German cities. But Sandys saw it as fitting into an ominous overall pattern.

Granted that they existed at all, what might such new weapons be? Long-range guns? This could be a logical extension of the Big Bertha of World War I. Pilotless aircraft? The Americans had already had fair success with something of the sort as far back as World War I. Later they dropped these experiments. Long-range rockets? Fantastic as it might seem, Sandys inclined to this view.

Duncan Sandys was not a man to be taken in easily. He was, in fact, the ideal choice for his present assignment. His father-in-law, Mr. Churchill, was pleased when the Chiefs of Staff had recommended him. Duncan Sandys knew something about rockets. In November 1940, as a major in the Royal Regiment of Artillery, he had been made commanding officer of the first Z, or rocket, battery in the British

Army. Although the unit was equipped only with modest anti-aircraft missiles, Sandys became interested in the potential of bigger rockets. He set out to learn what he could about them—and then his military career came to a sudden, violent end. Speeding toward night operations at Cardiff, his driver dozed at the wheel. The car smashed into a stone wall and Sandys was left with a crippling disablement to both feet. Now, as Under-Secretary at the Ministry of Supply, he was thinking about rockets again, this time with a sense of urgency.

Rockets were not really new weapons. The Chinese had repulsed invading Mongols with "arrows of flying fire" in 1232. Sir William Congreve had leveled the greater part of Copenhagen in 1807 with his solid-propellant rockets. The American national anthem contained a phrase about "the rocket's red glare." Tsiolkovsky, a Russian schoolteacher, had published a book in 1903 on the possibility of space travel by means of rockets. An American, Dr. Robert Goddard, had fired the world's first successful liquid-fuel rocket in 1926.

But what about the Germans? Had they really been able to advance beyond these primitive beginnings to a stage worth serious concern? A Professor Hermann Oberth had published *The Rocket into Interplanetary Space* in 1923 and this book, while small, was remarkable in detailing the technical groundwork for serious rocket development. His suspicions strengthened, Sandys put the Intelligence Services to work interviewing refugee scientists and combing through old German newspapers, magazines, military, and trade journals. This turned up some information, but none of it was startling. A group of young German rocket enthusiasts had formed the Society for Space Travel in the early thirties and had fired crude rockets from the Raketenflugplatz, an abandoned dump in Berlin. But their names meant nothing to Sandys' scientific advisers. The international scientific community was well aware of the identity of those German scientists who seemed capable of great scientific breakthroughs. None of them appeared to have shown any serious interest in rockets.

But then a captured German general, one of the thousands of prisoners of war who were being interrogated in the search for the facts, admitted that he had seen big rockets. He had not been overly impressed by them, but he had heard talk that they were designed to win the war for Germany. A second captured general confirmed what the first had said. Neither could provide details, and Sandys went back to the Secret Intelligence Service. The answer was as frustrating as before: Peenemünde could not be penetrated, and Intelligence's most highly placed contacts in the German government could provide no further information. Whatever was going on at Peenemünde was obviously a secret shared by those working there and a handful of the highest Nazi leaders.

Sandys turned again to his scientific advisers. They informed him that neither the British, the Americans, nor the Russians were working on anything more advanced than small rockets with limited range. Without underestimating German technical ingenuity, they seemed disinclined to believe that even a massive effort could bring Germany close to a long-range rocket that would work and could be manufactured in sufficient quantities to constitute an imminent threat. And yet the possibility that the Germans *were* on the verge of a breakthrough struck Sandys as too great to be ignored.

If the secret weapons he had been asked to investigate were indeed big rockets, to Sandys this meant trouble of the most serious kind. For—although it had no part in his investigation—another problem existed which was causing acute anxiety within the inner circle of Allied leaders, one which the general public was also unaware of. The atomic bomb project had gotten under way in earnest in the United States in the summer of 1942, but the insiders knew that two Germans—Otto Hahn and Fritz Strassmann—had been the first to discover the principle of uranium fission upon which the atom bomb would be based. This had happened in December 1938.

It was not known what the Germans had done with their head start, although it was known that they were conducting research in atomic energy. The thought of what could happen if Hitler got his hands on a long-range rocket or pilotless aircraft was unnerving in itself. But the thought of what could happen if they were equipped with atomic devices in their warheads struck Sandys as the most frightening possibility of the entire war.

He sat down and once again carefully reviewed the patchwork of available evidence—meager, confusing, but still alarming—and then presented his report to the War Cabinet, whose members came upon this sobering paragraph:

> It would appear that the Germans have for some time past been trying to develop a heavy rocket capable of bombarding an area from a very long range. This work has probably been proceeding side by side with the development of jet-propelled aircraft and airborne rocket torpedoes. Very little information is available about the progress of this development. However, such scanty evidence as exists suggests that it may be far advanced. London, in view of its size, is much the most likely target.

London *was* the most likely target. Given the limited accuracy at long range of the early rockets and "airborne rocket torpedoes," they could not be used effectively against specific military targets. They would have to be fired at random against large, crowded cities. The War Cabinet agreed with Sandys that the threat to London was serious but could not agree on countermeasures. The Norwegian plant which had been discovered to be shipping heavy water to Germany for atomic research had been blown up by saboteurs in February 1943. Peenemünde, a large, closely guarded installation in Germany itself, could not be given similar treatment. Sandys' plea that Peenemünde be attacked from the air was tabled. The Air Staff objected that it was far beyond the range of targets currently being attacked and that no real proof of rocket or any other secret weapon development existed to justify a dangerous and costly raid.

Sandys was directed to intensify his search for solid facts, to make maximum use of the only espionage tool that seemed capable of unlocking the secret of Peenemünde. Thwarted on the ground, the spies took to the air. Spitfires and Mosquitoes streaked high over the Baltic, switching on their cameras as they neared Usedom Island, searching for a sign, a confirmation of Sandys' suspicions.

It was not long in coming.

On June 23, 1943, a cloudless, sunlit day in the western Baltic, Flight Sergeant E.P.H. Peek returned with photographs that were as clear as the blue skies over Peenemünde. They were analyzed by Flight Officer Constance Babington-Smith, whose curiosity had been aroused by earlier photographs. She had been told to look out for "anything queer," and this time she found it: four small airplanes that were different from any she had ever seen. They had no tails and had left behind them a curious trail of dark streaks as they rose above the airfield.

Flight Lieutenant André Kenny and Wing Commander Hugh Hamshaw Thomas also found something queer in the same photographs. Two torpedo-like objects, about forty feet long, were caught by the camera's eye out in the brilliant sunshine, lying horizontally on what appeared to be long trailers. They were labeled by the British as actual rockets with a possible range of up to 130 miles. The tailless airplanes detected by Constance Babington-Smith were analyzed as being jet-propelled aircraft, and in later photographs she would detect "airborne rocket torpedoes."

Photographic espionage was intensified and soon revealed, popping up like measles all over the face of northern France, "work of an unexplained nature." It was surmised that these puzzling structures, all pointing toward London, might be firing points for the secret weapons. But the secret of the *exact* nature of these weapons still remained to be solved satisfactorily. The photographs definitely confirmed that experimental work was being done on three different kinds of unusual weapons but could give no indication of how and when they would be put into action, or in what order.

These questions caused anxious, spirited debate among the Prime Minister's scientific advisers. One group backed Duncan Sandys in believing that the greatest danger was in an attack by long-range rockets. Another equally influential group felt strongly that workable rockets could not be perfected for a long time to come and that pilotless aircraft were the more likely threat. A third group felt that the whole thing was a gigantic hoax designed to distract the main thrust of the Allied war effort, that the thousands of aerial photographs had uncovered nothing but ingenious dummies. Constance Babington-Smith described this early period of anxiety and lack of unanimity as "a time of frustrating confusion in the secret weapon investigation . . . a time of groping in the dark, of trying to lay foundations in a swamp."

The majority opinion, however, came round to Sandys' persistent advocacy of the view that London was in for a novel kind of attack from the air. Herbert Morrison, Minister for Home Security, considered the prospect of having to undertake a wholesale evacuation of metropolitan London. Something had to be done, and quickly. On June 29, Winston Churchill, following the recommendation of his Defence Committee, settled the matter of what should be done. Peenemünde would be attacked by Bomber Command at the first favorable opportunity. This would be a British operation; the Americans, for the present, would not be fully informed of the concern that the Sandys investigation had caused.

Bomber Command Headquarters, without any great show of enthusiasm for what it knew would be a nasty piece of work, carefully drew up its plan of attack. The first proposal, to send three waves over the target, was vetoed. Surprise must be the keynote of the raid. Destruction of the physical facilities at Peenemünde was not enough. Those strange objects that had been detected under the magnifying lenses of the Photo Interpretation Unit had been created by technicians. The only effective way to stop their work was to kill as many of them as possible. Three attack waves could not fulfill this objective, because the people not killed by the first wave would take shelter before the second and third could unload their high-explosive and fire bombs.

A single, massive, and dangerous strike by moonlight was called for. Its primary purpose was to kill the scientists and engineers, who, it was reasoned, would be asleep and unprotected within the Peenemünde installation.

# 2

## By moonlight

Major General Walter Dornberger, the officer in charge of rocket development for the German Army, stubbed out his after-dinner cigar, left the Hearth Room at Peenemünde, and walked through the blackout to his quarters.

It was August 17, 1943, and for him it had been a tiring day. The sun had scorched the white Baltic sands and turned the arid soil of Usedom into a steaming cauldron. As if this enervating humidity hadn't been enough, in the afternoon there had been an explosive argument between the development and production departments that had threatened to disrupt the rocket program. General Dornberger had been caught in the middle. He'd had to find a solution to the production bottleneck and then smooth the ruffled feelings of the directors involved.

Later, he had relaxed a little at dinner with Dr. Wernher von Braun, his engineering director; Dr. Ernest Steinhoff, his director of guidance and control; and Hanna Reitsch, the woman test pilot, their guest for the evening. But now Dornberger felt tired again as he walked through the sticky night air, recalling that, a few days before, the Air Ministry had warned him that an air raid might be in the offing. As he reached the visitors' quarters that he used when he came up from his main office in Berlin, ninety miles to the south, he heard the keening of the "early alarm."

It was not the first time he had heard it at Peenemünde, for British bombers normally grouped over the central Baltic for the run south to Berlin, and he was not overly alarmed. Peenemünde had not been attacked because it was a poor target, long and narrow, scattered along the coast, and it was protected by night fighters, heavy anti-aircraft guns, and a smoke screen. It was also beyond the range of British night fighters and radio-navigation beams, which meant that the bombers would have to come in alone and by moonlight. And there was a strict, faultless blackout which was, as usual, in effect on this night.

Then Dornberger noticed that the blackout had been slightly pierced. He saw, eerily lighting the roofs of camouflaged buildings, the faint but spreading beams of the moon —a full moon. He dashed into his room and telephoned air defense headquarters.

"Allied formations are massing over the central Baltic," he was told.

"Direction of approach?"

"Not yet known."

It was probably another raid on Berlin. In any case, there was nothing further that Dornberger could do. He prepared for bed, alone with his thoughts.

If Duncan Sandys could have shared those thoughts or been presented by the Secret Intelligence Service with the biography of this unknown major general of *Wa Pruef* 11, "Department of Special Ordnance Devices," he would have needed nothing more to unlock the secret of Peenemünde. And Sandys' already great concern would have multiplied many times.

Dornberger had been born in Giessen, a small university city near Frankfurt, where his father had been a pharmacist. Walter Dornberger had thought of becoming an architect, but in August 1914 he enlisted in the Army. In October 1918, as a lieutenant of artillery, he was captured by the 2nd Division of the United States Marine Corps and handed over to the French. He spent two years in a French prisoner-of-war camp, most of them in solitary confinement as a result of repeated escape attempts.

When he was released to a defeated Germany of inflation and unemployment, Dornberger found that there was no demand for untrained young lieutenants. He counted himself fortunate to be allowed to remain in a *Reichswehr* limited to 100,000 men by the Treaty of Versailles. He was sent to the University of Berlin, and after five years graduated with a mechanical engineering degree and was assigned to the Ballistics Branch of the Army Weapons Department. The assignment was not a plum. The Versailles Treaty specifically forbade the development of German artillery of over three inches in caliber. But the treaty had neglected to mention anything about rockets. In 1930, Captain Dornberger was given a job many ambitious career officers considered minor, thankless, and somewhat ludicrous: to build up, from nothing, a military rocket program.

Dornberger set up an experimental station at Kummersdorf West, eighteen miles south of Berlin. He enlisted the services of young civilian rocket enthusiasts who could not obtain backing for their primitive experiments from banks or private industry. On October 1, 1932, Dornberger hired a twenty-year-old student, Wernher von Braun, as his technical assistant.

Hitler came to power in 1933, but his lively and perceptive interest in weapons did not include rockets. Except for a brief visit, he ignored Dornberger and his Kummersdorf installation. But in 1934, General von Fritsch, commander in chief of the *Reichswehr,* witnessed a successful rocket-firing demonstration and extended his firm backing. His successor, General von Brauchitsch, transferred Dornberger and his ninety-man organization to new and larger facilities at Peenemünde, where encouraging progress was made on the A type of rocket.*

Hitler waited until a wet, chilly day in March 1939 before taking another look at what Dornberger was up to, and then he did not visit Peenemünde, but the original station at Kummersdorf. Von Braun wanted to explain to the Führer that the rocket could one day be used for space travel, but Dornberger sagely counseled him against this. The two men showed Hitler around and concentrated on the military potential of the long-range rockets still in the development stage. Hitler, looking tanned and fit, listened politely, but Dornberger felt that he was not overly impressed. Hitler was interested in weapons that would work in the present, not the possible future. After the successful *blitzkriegs* of 1939-40 against Poland and France, Hitler personally reduced Peenemünde's costly top priority. It was a decision that may have lost his war.

Walter Dornberger felt a stab of rage whenever he thought of that decision. In August 1943 he was being pressured to push through a crash program, now that it was obvious that the conventional weapons had failed. But if the Führer hadn't canceled the top priority in 1940, the rocket would be ready now. Not all of his memories were as discouraging as this, however. He could remember the high noon of a brilliant, cloudless day, October 3, 1942, when he had stood on the roof of the Measurement House and barked an order into his hand microphone: *"Start Frei!"* (Rocket Away!) After two previous test failures, an A-4 had blasted from its firing table nearly sixty miles high, attained a speed of 3,500 miles an hour, and fallen on target 120 miles away.

Dornberger had given a small party that night for Dr.

---

* *A* stood for *Aggregat,* an innocuous cover designation meaning unit, series, or prototype. A-1, which weighed 85 pounds and was about 4½ feet long, had been built in 1933. A-4 was the fourth model in the series.

Walter Thiel, von Braun, Steinhoff, Hermann Oberth, and a few other members of the staff. They had gotten a little drunk, but there was cause for celebration. The day's test had proved that the long-range missile was a practicable proposition. And since that particular A-4 had also been the first object made by man to curve into the borders of outer space, it proved that rocket power was practicable for space exploration.

Dornberger had made a short congratulatory speech in which he said: "Today the space ship is born!" Then he reminded his guests that their first job was to perfect the rocket as a weapon. He told von Braun, who was given to overexuberance, "I warn you that our headaches are by no means over—they're just beginning." Nevertheless, he went to bed that night feeling certain that he would get everything he needed to put the A-4 into mass production.

He had been right about the headaches. Top priority was not restored. The required supplies and technical personnel were slow in coming, and the meddling of party bureaucrats caused further delays.

But Dornberger had a friend at court. He kept pressing Albert Speer, Minister of Munitions, who had given the rocket program intelligent support, to intervene with the one man in Germany who could turn the A-4 into an operational weapon. In March 1943, Speer approached Hitler and reported back to Dornberger that the Führer was still not interested in extending his firm backing to the rocket program. The reason given baffled and enraged Dornberger. "The Führer," Speer reported, "has dreamed that no A-4 will ever reach England."

But the Führer must have had other dreams, Dornberger thought, because on July 7, 1943, Speer told Dornberger, von Braun, and Steinhoff to fly to Hitler's headquarters, Wolf's Lair, in East Prussia and to bring with them anything that could bolster their case for the A-4, including the filmed record of the successful test firing of October 3, 1942.

They ran the film, with von Braun doing the commentary, and this time the Führer was impressed. In contrast to their last confrontation, in March 1939, Hitler now seemed a tired man, his back bent, his shoulders hunched, his face drawn and pallid. But his eyes still seemed bright and strangely hypnotic as he rushed over to Dornberger as the film ended, pumped his hand, and said: "Why was it I could not believe in the success of your work? If we'd had these rockets in 1939 we'd never have had this war." Later he added: "I have had to apologize only to two men in my whole life. The first was Field Marshal von Brauchitsch. I did not listen to him when he told me again and again how important your research was. The second man is yourself. I never believed that your work would be successful."

Peenemünde was given the highest priority in the Third Reich. It came to Dornberger as a mixed blessing. He was suddenly being asked to recoup the lost years and bring off a unique scientific achievement in the face of wartime shortages, the steady advances of the Allied armies, and the threat of heavy bombing. Even in the quiet of a peacetime laboratory equipped with all the necessary matériel it would have been difficult to live up to the Führer's hopes, which were now so exaggerated that he thought the war could be won with what the Propaganda Ministry was already speaking of as "miracle weapons."

Dornberger was a rocket expert with a doctor's degree in mechanical engineering, but he was also a professional soldier and he could not believe that the present military situation could be radically changed by missiles carrying one ton of explosives 160 miles. There was a possibility, however, that if the A-4 test models could be rolled off the production lines as operational weapons within six months or a year, a stalemate could be created and an invasion force prevented from reaching the continent from English ports. General Dornberger intended to do his best to see that these goals were achieved—that is, if he was allowed to.

In early April 1943, Dornberger had had a visitor. The *Reichsführer* SS, Heinrich Himmler himself, had appeared for the first time at Peenemünde, despite the fact that it was a joint Army and Air Force installation and the SS had no responsibility there beyond guarding it.

Himmler did not have the disquieting effect on Dornberger that he had on most other people. The SS leader had impressed him as a good listener, a mild-mannered fellow wearing the pince-nez of a country schoolteacher and a quiet, thin-lipped smile. The *Reichsführer* SS had quietly looked around and said as he left: "Your work is interesting. Perhaps I can help. I'll come back."

He did return, on June 29, at the wheel of his own tiny armored car. After dinner he delivered a five-hour monologue to Dornberger, von Braun, and a few other senior members of the staff on history, philosophy, and the purposes of the war. The next day he witnessed two test launchings of the A-4; the first a miscarry, the second stunningly successful. He offered to intercede with Hitler on Peenemünde's behalf, and he still impressed Dornberger as an amiable, unemotional fellow.

Between Himmler's first and second visits, however, Dornberger had discovered a dismaying development. His friend, Colonel Leo Zanssen, for many years the station commander at Peenemünde and a career Army officer of impeccable background, had been dismissed on accusations leveled by Himmler himself. And Dornberger had heard reports that certain SS officers, who knew nothing about rockets, were saying that Dornberger was responsible for the delays in the rocket program which he had started and directed for thirteen years.

What could the *Reichsführer* SS have in mind? What was

going on behind that inscrutable exterior? The A-4 program was an Army Weapons Department undertaking and headed by Dornberger as an Army officer. He knew, however, that the SS had its own Weapons Department and that all over the Third Reich the SS was gradually moving in on the Army's traditional functions.

If Himmler did have designs on Peenemünde, he would encounter in Dornberger a stubborn obstacle to fulfilling them. At forty-eight Dornberger was a stocky man of medium height, clean-shaven, with smooth pinkish skin, iron-gray hair, and a balding pate. Only a few of his closest associates knew that his thinning hair and unwrinkled skin were evidence of both his resilience and membership in the inner circle of rocket pioneers.

In 1932, at the Kummersdorf Proving Ground, he had made a mistake. He was always in a hurry to get things done and had tried to dismantle a solid rocket containing a black powder charge by using a steel hammer and chisel instead of copper. As Dornberger worked on the rocket, sparks from the copper ignited the powder. The charge went off in his face.

Doctors at the Berlin military hospital said that he would not live and that this might be a blessing. His burns were hideous and beyond the healing capabilities of the plastic surgery of the time. He spent a year in the hospital, alone except for an orderly. The two of them concocted a home remedy for the treatment of burns.

For ten hours each day the orderly patiently smeared Dornberger's face and arms with butter, then picked the hundreds of tiny flecks of black powder out of his skin, one by one. Dornberger survived to continue his direction of the rocket program. His pink, unwrinkled skin made those meeting him for the first time think wrongly that he had not a worry in the world. But anyone who could survive a rocket charge blowing up in his face, Dornberger may well have thought, could survive Himmler.

The early air-raid alarm was still keening when he fell into a deep sleep within five minutes of entering his room. It was shortly after midnight.

Wernher von Braun was also asleep. He had left the Hearth Room with Hanna Reitsch and Dr. Ernst Steinhoff, who, as director of guidance and control, was one of the key department chiefs at Peenemünde. Dr. Steinhoff had gone home to the family living quarters. Von Braun, a bachelor, had escorted Hanna Reitsch to the car that would take her to the visitors' quarters at the Luftwaffe Experimental Station three miles away. Fräulein Reitsch, the only civilian ever to be awarded the Iron Cross, First Class, was scheduled to test-fly in the morning the Messerschmitt-163, a revolutionary rocket-powered fighter plane. Von Braun had known her since they had both graduated from an advanced gliding school in 1932. He wished her luck with the dangerous test flight and then hurried to his own quarters. He, too, had heard the early alarm but had paid no special attention to it and went to sleep. As a civilian, air-raid precautions were not his responsibility. He was, at thirty-one, the technical director of *Heeresversuchstelle* (Army Experimental Station) Peenemünde and had more than enough problems of his own to worry about.

Half a mile away from von Braun's bachelor quarters was the *Siedlung* (Settlement), where four thousand German technicians and their families lived, including Dr. Steinhoff and Dr. Walther Thiel. Dr. Thiel, his wife and four children had been asleep for three hours. Work began at 7 A.M., and Dr. Thiel insisted on a good night's sleep. He had a crucial job. He was in charge of rocket propulsion, had developed the A-4 motor, and now had to refine it. The Thiel family slept soundly. The only sound in the comfortable two-story house fronting the Baltic came from the window curtains, which fluttered in a slight breeze.

# 25  [By moonlight]

South of the Thiel home, in a camp hidden in a pine forest, five hundred Russian prisoners of war, who were used for roadbuilding and other heavy construction jobs, had been asleep since the 9 P.M. curfew. But south of them, in the huts of the Trassenheide camp, where six hundred Polish civilian slave laborers were quartered, at least two of the Poles could not have been asleep. They were the men who had smuggled sketches of Peenemünde and reports of the weird sights they had glimpsed there out to Polish Home Army Intelligence. As a reward for their work, they had been advised to leave Peenemünde on this night. The Trassenheide camp, however, was surrounded by SS guards armed with machine pistols, electrically charged barbed wire, and Doberman pinschers. An attempt to escape from this complex, or even to warn the other Poles, would serve no purpose except to alert the SS that something unexpected was going to happen.

British Bomber Command had been directed to destroy the suspected center of German secret weapon development at "the first favorable opportunity." The chance came on this night of August 17, 1943. At 9:50 P.M., Wing Commander J. H. Searby and his six-man crew took off in their Lancaster from the Norfolk coast. Behind them flew 597 Lancaster and Halifax heavy bombers of the Royal Air Force.

Following a carefully rehearsed plan, Searby flew high over Denmark, then dipped so low over the moonlit Baltic that he could see whitecaps on the water. He later recalled that "an aircraft flying low over the sea is not easy to discern even in bright moonlight, and we were far to low for the big radars on the mainland to pick us up." Shortly before midnight, Searby approached the narrow peninsula upon whose northern tip Peenemünde was located.

It was a fine summer night, clear except for a few sheets of cloud. Searby had been briefed on the night fighters and heavy anti-aircraft batteries known to be defending the target. It had to be a hellishly important one to justify this kind of long-range operation without fighter escort, Searby may well have thought. Before taking off, he had heard reports of the Americans' long-range raid on Regensburg-Schweinfurt earlier that day. It had been carried out, beginning at dawn on what had been a bright, sunny August day, without the cover of fighter planes, whose fuel tanks could not take them either to Regensburg-Schweinfurt or Peenemünde. Sixty American heavy bombers had not returned.

Air Marshal Sir Arthur Harris, Chief of Bomber Command, however, had made it quite clear that this risky night operation against Peenemünde was important, so much so that if it was not completely successful it would be repeated until the target was eradicated. "Bomber" Harris knew why it was important, but the target was so secret that the crews themselves had been told only that "some specialized radar equipment" was being made at Peenemünde and had to be destroyed.

J. H. Searby had been appointed Master Bomber. It was his job to fly over the target and continue to circle it during the entire raid, directing the bombing force by radio-telephone. Three substitute Master Bombers were ready to replace him if, as he dryly noted, "we were unable to perform this work as a result of interference by the enemy."

Preceding Searby, a flight of Mosquitoes flew over Peenemünde without dropping a single bomb, following the southerly course of previous raids on Berlin. The Luftwaffe night fighters fell for the feint, flashed after the Mosquitoes to intercept them before they could strike the capital, and left Peenemünde undefended. Then, as the Pathfinders, whose job it was to illuminate the target and mark the aiming points, dropped their white, yellow, green, and red marker flares, Searby turned out to sea, wheeled, and led the main force in. He saw the smoke screen begin to drift over the target and anti-aircraft shells bursting near his Lancaster. The Germans had at last realized what was coming.

"We were now ready," Searby reported, "for the operation to commence."

General Dornberger was awakened by a terrific blast. He sat up to find his bed covered with broken glass from what had been windowpanes. He heard the anti-aircraft fire, grabbed the telephone on his night table, and called the concrete command shelter. The line was busy. He vaulted out of bed, threw his tunic over his pajamas, and in slippers walked over a carpet of broken glass into the night. He was greeted by a scene that, he was to record, "had a sinister and appalling beauty of its own."

Searchlights stabbed into a night sky full of stars. The smoke canisters surrounding Peenemünde had been set off too late to be fully effective, but drifting clouds of mist now mixed with the brilliance of the full moon and the rainbow colors of the dropping marker flares. There were red tongues of roaring fire everywhere. And Dornberger's ears were assaulted by a symphony of anti-aircraft fire, exploding bombs, and the steady drone of four-engine bombers. He wondered angrily where the Luftwaffe night fighters were as he dashed the few yards to the command shelter.

He spotted von Braun in front of the concrete bunker, his blond hair white with ashes, his broad chin pointed upward. A thermite incendiary exploded and hissed over their heads and they flung themselves into a long, brilliantly lit room filled with stunned, immobile people. Dornberger telephoned the chief air-raid warden and got a status report that confirmed his worst suspicions. This was a full-scale, all-out attack. He began snapping orders. "Von Braun, get over to the construction bureau. Take everybody here and round up the Luftwaffe labor gang. Try to check the fires, but if you can't, get the drawings and records out to a safe place. Now!"

Without a word, knowing the importance of what was in the construction bureau, von Braun dashed out of the shelter into the flaming, thunderous night. His face a mass of sweat from the humidity and the inferno of darting flames, he was occasionally jarred to the ground by the impact of exploding bombs. Dodging craters and falling pieces of hot, twisted metal, he ran to salvage the papers that represented thirteen years of his life's work. After him, through a ghostly fog created by the smoke screen mixed with thick clouds of smoke from the raging fires, ran scores of helpers, their faces made black and unrecognizable by the swirling soot.

Dornberger followed von Braun out of the shelter and headed in a different direction on a quick inspection tour of the Measurement House, assembly workshop, component workshop, and finally the burning guesthouse, in which he had been sleeping soundly barely an hour before. Dornberger suddenly remembered that inside were his family papers, stamp collection, and prized shotguns, all of which he had brought up from Berlin, intending to store them in the nearby countryside for safekeeping.

He climbed through a bathroom window and picked his way over fallen rafters to the living room and bedroom, throwing everything he could put his hands on out into the grass. He tucked his shotguns and hunting gear under his arms, then heard a door split apart and saw red tentacles of fire reaching for him. Dropping everything, he wrapped himself in a blanket and flung himself out into the open through flames circling an open window.

Overhead, Wing Commander Searby wondered when the diverted night fighters would come streaking back. He reasoned that the clearness of the night, the brilliant illumination of the fires and full moon, and the unusually low level—8,000 feet—at which the raid was being carried out would give the Luftwaffe an opportunity to score a record number of kills.

He flew back and forth over the target, directing the bomber force, evaluating results, making adjustments. H-hour had been midnight, when the first group of yellow markers—followed by a bright red target indicator—had gone down over the housing area where Intelligence had calculated that the technicians lived. Searby thought they were well placed and "right on the pin." As anti-aircraft shells thudded around "William," his Lancaster, he "observed the fall of the high explosive and incendiary bombs in good concentration—fires were starting and beginning to spread."

The sleeping Dr. Walther Thiel, director of rocket propulsion, his wife and four children never saw the spreading fires. A high-explosive bomb scored a direct hit on their wooden beach house and turned it into a flaming mausoleum.

Dr. Ernst Steinhoff, director of guidance and control, his wife and three children dashed into the cellar of their duplex house just before it was struck by a land mine. The house collapsed over them, but, coughing and fighting for air in the cramped cellar, they survived unharmed.

Hundreds of the other technicians and their families in the Settlement fled into the night. They flung themselves into the protective slit trenches before their homes or ran over the sand dunes to Zinnowitz as the thousand-pounders and stick and phosphorus incendiaries rained down around them.

The Russian POW's and the Polish laborers in the Trassenheide camp could not flee. Direct hits shattered and set their wooden huts on fire, forcing panic-stricken men—scores of them turned into torches by the hissing incendiaries—to claw at the barbed-wire enclosures. As they tried to crawl through the wire, the SS guards waved them back and, when they did not obey, set Doberman pinschers on them or used machine guns. None of the foreign workers escaped during the confusion of the raid to bring any further information about Peenemünde to British Intelligence, and the reports from the two technically trained members of the Polish Underground stopped after this night.

After the living quarters of the German technicians and then the research buildings had been marked and bombed, Searby encountered difficulty in observing the effects of the raid because of the fires and dense clouds of smoke rising from the target area. But at fifty minutes after H-hour he saw Lancasters and Halifaxes exploding around him and going down in flames. The Luftwaffe night fighters, which had been drawn away by the feint at Berlin, had now returned. It was time to radio the main force to leave.

Searby took his final run, his fourteenth, over the target and swung out low over the sea. "William" was attacked by an ME-110, but the German fighter was an old model and Searby's rear gunner brought it down with a good burst. Others in the armada of heavy bombers were not so fortunate. By now the flak ships in Peenemünde Harbor had pin-pointed the bombers passing above them and took their toll. The bright moonlight, which had been such an aid to the bombing, gave the fast Luftwaffe night fighters first-class conditions for scoring their kills among the slower bombers, which were protected only by their own guns. Searby made it back to England, but forty Royal Air Force Bombers, with 240 crewmen, were caught by the German fighters and anti-aircraft guns and destroyed.

The Peenemünde raid had been undertaken in the knowledge that it would be dangerous and costly, and it was. But those who returned from it felt that it had been successful and praised Master Bomber Searby's technique. Squadron Leader Huntley-Wood of No. 207 Squadron could not assess the effects of his own work "owing to the intensity of the bombing." But Huntley-Wood thought "the target had the appearance of being well and truly hit."

Pilot Officer Fitzgerald of 207 Squadron, who had come in at the end of the raid, was optimistic. "A return visit to Peenemünde by Bomber Command will be unnecessary," he reported to ground interrogators. Flight Lieutenant Mickey MacMichelmore of No. 44 (Rhodesia) Squadron perhaps best summed up the feeling of those who returned from Peenemünde: "An excellent prang has been achieved."

# 3

## Crossbow

In England an analysis of the effects of the raid was immediately begun. The conclusions reached were optimistic. Air Chief Marshal Sir Charles Portal, Chief of the Air Staff, felt that development at Peenemünde has been set back at least six months. This view was shared by the Allied leaders until the war's end.

At Peenemünde itself, General Dornberger conducted a survey of his own. To his knowledgeable eye, the surprise attack appeared a punishing blow. It had left rubble-strewn streets, blast-blackened buildings, masses of twisted girders, and other scenes which caused him to note: "Death had reaped a rich harvest here." But it had not set back development for six months. Six weeks was a more likely figure, according to Dornberger's on-the-spot estimate. Von Braun had survived and saved the all-important blueprints. Some of the most critical installations—the test stands, wind tunnel, Measurement House—had not been hit. "Material damage to the works, contrary to first impressions, was surprisingly small," Dornberger recorded.

The Settlement, however, where the four thousand technicians and their families had lived, was a desolate ruin. On a sunlit Saturday morning, August 21, 1943, a mass funeral service was held at Peenemünde, presided over by a Lutheran minister and a Catholic priest. Seven hundred and thirty-five charred corpses were interred in common graves hastily dug along the wrecked railroad tracks. But Dornberger noted that the majority of those killed were Russian POW's and Polish laborers from Trassenheide. One hundred and seventy-eight German technicians had been lost. Of these, Dr. Walther Thiel alone, with his unique knowledge of rocket engines, would be difficult to replace. Dornberger, however, did not underestimate the meaning of the raid. The British could not know exactly what was going on at Peenemünde, but they had learned enough to be willing to pay a brutally high price to destroy it. They had failed, but the bombers would return unless extensive changes were made.

There would be no attempt, henceforth, to manufacture rockets at Peenemünde; this would be transferred to the Harz Mountains of central Germany. The supersonic wind tunnel would be transferred to Kochel in the Bavarian Alps. Test firings and the training of Army firing crews would be carried out in southern Poland, beyond the range of heavy bombers. Some necessary testing and all development work would continue at Peenemünde, but the Settlement would be abandoned and the technicians dispersed over other parts of Usedom Island. Repairs would be made to essential buildings only, activity would be kept inside during the day when the reconnaissance planes appeared, and camouflage would be put up. Everything possible would be done to create the illusion that Peenemünde had been destroyed. The measures succeeded to the extent that the bombers did not return for another nine months.

Dornberger's rocket program, however, was not the only project under development on the shores of the western Baltic. The true meaning of Peenemünde was to baffle Allied Intelligence until after D-day, and its secrets would not be fully unlocked until the war's end. Duncan Sandys had been correct in identifying Peenemünde as the center of German secret weapon development. It contained, however, not one, but two separate and independent development installations.

Peenemünde West, as opposed to the station Dornberger headed three miles away, was principally concerned with developing manned and unmanned jet planes and was operated by the German Air Force. The ME-163 and other models of manned jets, while much more advanced than anything the Allies were developing, were not—strictly speaking—secret weapons. But another Luftwaffe undertaking, the Fi-103, was. This midget, pilotless aircraft would eventually be known to history as the buzz bomb, doodlebug, flying bomb, V-1. Its development center had been completely missed in the attack of August 17.

The other part of Peenemünde was, of course, the Experimental Station operated by the German Army. It was here that Dornberger and von Braun were working on something vastly different and more complex—a wingless, long-range rocket that would become known to British Intelligence as Big Ben and to history as V-2. It had nothing whatever to do with V-1, except that it was the second in what Hitler hoped would be a long series of *Vergeltungswaffen* (reprisal or retaliation weapons), a designation concocted by Goebbels' Propaganda Ministry.

The Luftwaffe's V-1 was nothing more than an ingeniously contrived aerial torpedo with wings. On the other hand, the Army's V-2 was the world's first true guided missile. It loomed as a really new and terrifying weapon because, unlike V-1, it was supersonic; when perfected it would approach its target silent and unseen and there could be no defense against it.

There was a great deal of wasteful rivalry between the Luftwaffe and the Army concerning the merits of the two secret weapons. The Commander in Chief of the Luftwaffe, Reich Marshal Goering, claimed that V-1 should be given priority over V-2 because it had about the same range, could carry as big a warhead, and, since it was a simpler mechanism, could be mass-produced for one tenth the cost. This ignored the larger implications of V-2, but Goering had a valid point.

The Long-Range Bombardment Commission had in fact convened at Peenemünde on May 26, 1943, to determine—in view of the growing shortage of raw materials and trained technicians—which of the secret weapons should be given the go-ahead and which eliminated. It had been an anxious day for Dornberger, who could have seen his rocket program canceled right there. But during the comparative demonstrations, V-1 had encountered technical difficulties, while V-2 had two perfect launchings. It was decided to put both weapons into mass production and, if possible, to use them in conjunction.

Of these subtleties, of course, British Intelligence remained unaware through the fall of 1943. Intelligence had learned enough, however, to realize that a race, a silent war, had begun. Its existence was kept secret from the general public, from the men driving back the German armies in Russia and Italy with conventional weapons, and from the pilots carrying out daily saturation bombings of German cities and industrial targets. Only an inner circle of Allied leaders knew that new and nightmarish German weapons actually existed, and that if they could be put into action in large quantities before the cross-Channel invasion of France the entire pattern of the war could be changed.

Duncan Sandys had made his point. He remained an adviser on rockets, but his special investigation now became an eyes-only priority project and was transferred to the Air Staff, which was given responsibility for both intelligence and countermeasures. The Air Staff continued to find the exact nature of the threat an unsettling riddle. Would the attack come from rockets or flying bombs, or both? How accurate were these weapons? How much destruction could they be expected to cause? When would they be put into action, and in what quantities? Peenemünde had been bombed, but could the firing points be located and destroyed before D-day? If not, could the invasion base of England, and its civilian population, be defended against the secret weapons?

On September 25, 1943, Dr. R. V. Jones, Chief of the Scientific Intelligence Branch of the Air Ministry, attempted to supply some answers to Winston Churchill:

> Much information has been collected. Allowing for the inaccuracies which often occur in individual accounts, they form a coherent picture which despite the bewildering effect of propaganda has but one explanation: the Germans have been conducting an extensive research into long-range rockets at Peenemünde. Their experiments have naturally encountered difficulties, which may still be holding up production. Although Hitler would press the rockets into service at the earliest possible moment, that moment is probably still some months ahead.[1]

A month later, on October 25, the Prime Minister communicated his anxiety to President Roosevelt:

> I ought to let you know that during the last six months evidence has continued to accumulate from many sources that the Germans are preparing an attack on England, particularly London, by means of very long-range rockets which may conceivably weigh sixty tons and carry an explosive charge of ten to twenty tons. For this reason we raided Peenemünde, which was their main experimental station. . . .
> Scientific opinion is divided as to the practicability of making rockets of this kind, but I am personally as yet unconvinced that they cannot be made. We are in close touch with your people . . . and all possible work is being done. The expert committee which is following this business thinks it possible that a heavy though premature and short-lived attack might be made in the middle of November, and that the main attack would be attempted in the New Year [1944]. . . .[2]

The Prime Minister was further disquieted to learn from British agents in France and the French Underground that, despite the massive attack on Peenemünde, the strange buildings in the Pas-de-Calais and on Cherbourg Peninsula—the "work of an unexplained nature" detected in earlier aerial photographs—were still going up. They were of two types. The so-called "large Sites" were gigantic structures, mainly underground, with steel and concrete walls at least thirty feet thick. One of them, at Watten, was described by General Lewis Brereton of the U. S. Army Air Forces as "more extensive than any concrete constructions we have in the United States, with the possible exception of Boulder Dam."

The second, and smaller, type were long, low, narrow buildings of heavy concrete with one end curved. From the air they resembled a giant ski laid on edge and came to be known as "Ski Sites." Near the ski-shaped buildings were three rectangular buildings and a platform about thirty feet long and twelve feet wide which appeared to be an inclined ramp with its major axis pointing toward London. That both the "Large Sites" and "Ski Sites" were firing points by now seemed an obvious and jarring fact. "They are very well camouflaged and hard to locate," General Brereton noted in his diary. "Every effort is being made to keep all information in connection with the . . . targets top secret so as not to cause panic among the public. On orders of the Prime Minister himself these targets can be referred to in the press only as 'military objectives,' in a way heightening the mystery about them."

Mr. Churchill asked Sir Stafford Cripps, Minister of Aircraft Production, to study the secret weapon problem in depth and to recommend a solution. On November 17, 1943, Sir Stafford presented his conclusions:

It would seem that the order of probability from the purely experimental point of view is: (1) Large glider bombs. (2)

Pilotless aircraft. (3) Small long-range rockets. (4) Large long-range rockets.

The R.A.F. raid on Peenemünde was undoubtedly of the greatest value, and has set back developments, whatever they may be, for the long-range offensive weapon.

There is no doubt that the Germans are doing their utmost to perfect some long-range weapon, and the new unexplained structures in Northern France are certainly most suspicious, unless we can assign some other use to them. Under these circumstances I feel we should make all reasonable preparations to cope with the consequences if and when the attack materialises, though there is no evidence of its materialisation before the New Year [1944] at the earliest.[3]

Churchill found that this report "certainly left much in doubt." Then, on aerial photographs of Peenemünde taken on November 28, 1943, Flight Officer Constance Babington-Smith detected "a tiny cruciform shape, set exactly on the lower end of . . . inclined rails—a midget aircraft actually in a position for launching." The doubts vanished. The inclined rails seen at Peenemünde tallied with the ramps seen at the "Ski Sites" in northern France. They were launching ramps, all pointed toward England, for the midget aircraft, the flying bomb, V-1. The ski-shaped structures nearby were meant for storing the flying bombs. It thus appeared that the attack would come from pilotless aircraft first, because no launching sites for the long-range rocket could be definitely detected, unless the "Large Sites" were meant for this purpose. But there were only eight of these, while by mid-December sixty-nine "Ski Sites" had been discovered by aerial reconnaissance.

In December the informal operations against the German secret weapons which had begun in April with the Sandys investigation were formalized as *Crossbow*. This code name "was used to designate Anglo-American operations against all phases of the German long-range weapons programme—operations against German research, experimentation, manufacture, construction of launching sites, and the transportation and firing of finished missiles, and also against missiles in flight, once they had been fired." [4] To direct this undertaking a *Crossbow* Committee was established, and its task was deemed so important that it was headed by Winston Churchill himself.

As soon as "Large Sites" and "Ski Sites" were identified by aerial reconnaissance or the French Underground, they were attacked by Bomber Command and the American Eighth and Ninth Air Forces. The crews, if they wondered why they were being diverted from their primary targets in Germany, were told they were attacking "special military installations." Plans were made for the defense of southern England with barrage balloons, radar-controlled anti-aircraft guns, and fighter planes. Herbert Morrison, Minister for Home Security, again was faced with the prospect of having to evacuate perhaps a million people from Greater London. The Anglo-American staff under Lieutenant General Sir Frederick Morgan, which was far along in its planning for *Operation Overlord,* the cross-Channel invasion of France, was faced with an equally disturbing prospect. In that December of 1943, no sane man could believe that the Germans would win the war. Two Allied armies were inching up the Italian peninsula. The burden of fighting the bulk of the German land forces still fell to the Russians, and they were bleeding Germany's armed strength in the field. The time was coming for the left jaw of the pincer to be applied, an attack from the west on occupied France. But what would become of his precise *Overlord* plans, General Morgan wondered, if the projected assembly areas and ports of southern England were hit by a sudden, massive bombardment in the coming spring?

The intensity of the *Crossbow* air attacks were increased. In March 1944, over four thousand tons of bombs were dropped on *Crossbow* targets in northern France. But the strange construction work kept pace with the bombings. In the absence of exact knowledge of what was happening, rumors were reported by Allied Intelligence. The Germans were going to fire huge tanks of poison gas to annihilate every inhabitant of Great Britain; they were going to bombard London with gigantic containers filled with a fatal "Red Death"; the curious structures on the French coast were really refrigerating apparatuses, designed to stop R.A.F. bombing by dropping ice clouds over England; the Germans had a rocket that could be fired from Berlin to New York. All of the rumors were later proved to be fantasies, except for the last one; a transoceanic ballistic missile *was* being developed at Peenemünde. It was called A-9, but in late 1943 it was still on the drawing boards.

In a tense atmosphere compounded of fantasy and a disturbing amount of fact, the Allied insiders found themselves plagued by another grim mystery. They had a crude knowledge of German rocket and flying-bomb development. But they knew next to nothing of the progress the Germans might have made with their head start in atomic research. General Leslie Groves, head of the Manhattan Project, knew that the time had come to find out. He organized the Alsos scientific intelligence mission. It would be sent first into Italy and then into other parts of continental Europe on the heels of the liberating armies.

The Allied scientific community, unlike the general public, was aware of the danger posed by German atomic capability. The prospect of a new kind of long-range missile that might conceivably carry an atomic warhead was something to cause sleepless nights to anyone in the British Isles permitted to have an understanding of the problem. Even American scientists were not immune to a certain feeling of panic. Samuel Goudsmit, professor of physics at Northwestern University, who was chosen as the scientific leader of the Alsos mission, learned that some of the men assigned to the

Manhattan Project at the University of Chicago were so uneasy that they had begun to send their families into the country. He also heard rumors that "scientific instruments were
set up around Chicago to detect the radioactivity if and when
the Germans attacked."

It would be at least six months to a year before the Alsos
mission could expect to enter France and Germany to determine whether there was any real foundation for this
anxiety about a German atomic bomb. Meanwhile, the very
real threat posed by the long-range weapons which were definitely known to exist haunted the Allied leaders even
while they were directing a steady march of victories.

It was, Mr. Churchill realized, imperative to discover exactly what these rockets and flying bombs might be capable
of doing in the near future; the *Crossbow* air attacks were
not enough. The job was handed to British Intelligence,
which was asked to pull off one of the most difficult espionage
operations of all time. The assignment was to locate one of
the Peenemünde scientists, all of whose names remained
unknown, pluck him from the midst of his SS guards, and
induce him to tell the Air Ministry everything he knew. If
this tall order could not be filled, the secondary objective
would be to capture one of the secret weapons and somehow
get it to England for minute analysis.

The world's finest intelligence service, with contacts extending into the *Abwehr* and the German General Staff itself, had at last been given a problem for which it could find
no solution. Elaborate SS security measures foiled all attempts to locate, much less capture, one of the scientists or
secret weapons. Peenemünde itself seemed so quiet that
there were those who took the hopeful view that the August
raid had indeed had indeed put a stop to secret weapon development. There was only one faint glimmer of useful intelligence in the unrewarding darkness, and it did not come
until the Christmas season of 1943.

Polish Home Army Intelligence, Cracow District, passed on to London a small but curious piece of news. There had been a tightening of security measures in the SS training camp at Blizna-Pustkow, 170 miles west of Warsaw. All the Poles living in the area had been ejected, a railway line had been built right into the camp, an airfield, hangars, and a workshop constructed, and the whole complex camouflaged and then fortified with heavy anti-aircraft guns.

All this struck the Polish Underground as an unusual amount of activity to be suddenly taking place in a routine training camp. The Underground continued to watch and to send further reports on the increased activity to London. British Intelligence had indicated to Churchill that a rocket attack might be expected by January 1944. The predicted date passed without incident. But in early March 1944, when plans for the Normandy landings were nearing completion, one of the Polish reports caused more than a little excitement at British Intelligence Headquarters.

An Underground worker with the code name of "Makary" had dared to crawl right up to the railway line leading into the Blizna camp. He claimed to have seen, mounted on a flatcar of unusual length and heavily guarded by SS troops in full battle regalia, "an object which, though covered by a tarpaulin, bore every resemblance to a monstrous torpedo."

British Intelligence immediately suspected that the "monstrous torpedo" was a rocket and that Blizna* was a new test firing range. Efforts to confirm these suspicions, however, would be frustrated until a month before D-day. Shielded from the reconnaissance planes and heavy bombers by distance and weather, and from the detailed scrutiny of the Polish Underground by SS guards, Walter Dornberger, Wernher von Braun, and their engineers were driving ahead

* Called *Heidelager* by the Germans.

with the A-4* at Blizna all through the winter of 1943-44. Their progress, however—though British Intelligence could not know it at the time—was being slowed by formidable problems that would have a direct bearing on when the A-4 would be put into action.

One of von Braun's problems was the danger to his own life posed by his experiments. At a test launch at Blizna one day in February 1944, he observed the rocket from a distance of barely three hundred yards, standing behind the crude shelter of a brick observation point. The A-4 was ignited, rose a few feet, then exploded into a cloud of orange flame. Von Braun pitched forward on frozen turf, burying his face in snow, as hot, twisted pieces of metal fell around him.

General Dornberger joined von Braun and went over with him, wearily and a little impatiently, the many possible reasons for the failure, which was only one among many. Ever since the launchings had been transferred to the overland range at Blizna troubles had come, according to Dornberger, "thick and fast. Shot after shot went wrong and faced us with apparently insoluble problems."

Dornberger instructed von Braun to return to Peenemünde and try once again to discover why hardly 20 percent of the rockets—which had tested so well when fired over the Baltic—were hitting their land targets in southern Poland. Then Dornberger got into his staff car and was driven to another in the endless series of conferences with important persons who now visited Blizna to see at first hand how the rocket program—which had become a top-priority undertaking in the Third Reich—was progressing.

It was difficult for Dornberger to explain to these eager amateurs why most of the rockets were exploding shortly

---

* *Fernrakete Aggregat-4* (Long-Range Rocket A-4) was dubbed V-2 by the Propaganda Ministry when it was put into action. Its developers never referred to it as anything but A-4.

after launching or breaking up just before reaching the planned impact point. Few of them could comprehend that the A-4 was a complex scientific instrument that would have been difficult to perfect in the leisurely quiet of a peace-time research institute. But it would have to be perfected under the trying wartime conditions now prevailing, Dornberger knew, and soon. Time was running out. The Russians were driving at Smolensk and Kiev. They might break through and overrun the Blizna range in two months. There were persistent reports that the Anglo-American forces would attempt a cross-Channel invasion of France in the coming spring or summer. "Authority was pressing us hard; we had to work fast," Dornberger later wrote. "Visitors from headquarters drove away with long faces. I felt too desperate myself to be able to reassure them." He was certain, however, that the technical difficulties could be solved in time, provided that the bureaucrats from the maze of overlapping and competing organizations that were now "springing up like mushrooms after rain" left the solutions to men who had spent their lives developing rockets.

Of all the outsiders who were trying to horn in on the rocket program, Dr. Hans Kammler caused Dornberger the greatest concern. *SS Brigadeführer* (Brigade General) Kammler, chief of the building branch of the SS Main Office, had been placed in charge of all construction work for the A-4 program in September 1943 by Himmler himself. Until now, construction had been an Army responsibility. Now the SS had insinuated itself in a modest way into a project operated by the Army Weapons Department. General Dornberger suspected that Kammler and the SS were not going to limit their interest in the A-4 to construction work. Dornberger's suspicions would shortly be confirmed.

After the test failure, Wernher von Braun, following Dornberger's instructions to return to the research laboratories at Peenemünde, flew his Messerschmitt-108 Typhoon from Blizna to the Experimental Station. It was a bumpy ride, with visibility poor because of whirling snow and ice forming on the plane's windows. It was dark, and von Braun was three hours overdue when he appeared in his office. He asked his secretary, Fräulein Beise, to order coffee and sandwiches sent up from the mess and to tell his department chiefs to join him for an all-night session. Fräulein Beise paused and then handed him a telephone message that had come in two hours before.

The message was from Himmler. The *Reichsführer SS* requested the technical director of Army Experimental Station Peenemünde to come to his headquarters. Von Braun was surprised and disquieted. This had never happened before; thus far, in fact, he had managed to stay out of the political infighting between the Army on the one hand and the SS and Nazi Party on the other. Nevertheless, he knew that Himmler's request was an order. He would have to put aside urgent work on the A-4's technical problems and obey it.

The *Reichsführer SS*, Minister of the Interior, Commander in Chief of the Reserve Army, Chief of the Gestapo and all German Police, Heinrich Himmler, who was now the second most powerful man in Germany, had his main office at Prinz Albrecht Strasse 8 in Berlin. But recently he had taken to following the war on the eastern front from Hochwald in East Prussia, and it was to this field headquarters that von Braun flew the next day. He still did not know why Himmler wanted to see him alone; the SS was in charge of security at Peenemünde and Blizna but, apart from Kammler's recent appointment as chief of building, had little connection with the rocket program.

It was with what von Braun later described as "considerable trepidation" that he entered Himmler's office. The *Reichsführer SS* was seated behind a simple wooden desk,

wiping the thick lenses of his eyeglasses with a brown service handkerchief. Von Braun felt an odd sense of relief when
he caught sight of Himmler, who struck him as looking like
"a country schoolteacher" and "as mild-mannered a villain
as ever cut a throat." It was difficult to believe the stories
one heard about the man, for his appearance did not inspire
awe or fear. Nevertheless, von Braun was indefinably ill at
ease as Himmler politely motioned him to a chair and opened
the conversation. It was a scene von Braun would have reason
to remember in later years.

"It's good to see you again, Dr. von Braun," Himmler said.
"I'm sorry that I had to call you away from your important
work, and I wouldn't have done so if it weren't for a
matter of the utmost importance. I have been informed that
you're having trouble with the A-4."

"Nothing that we can't solve in time, *Reichsführer*."

"That's just the point. Time is running out. I hope you
realize that your A-4 rocket has ceased to be a toy and that
the whole German people eagerly await the mystery weapon.
As for you, I can imagine that you've been immensely
handicapped by Army red tape. Why not join my staff?
Surely you know that no one has such ready access to the
Führer, and I promise you vastly more effective support than
those hidebound generals can give you. The Führer is losing
confidence in the Army."

"*Reichsführer*, I couldn't ask for a better chief than General Dornberger," von Braun replied. "Such delays as we're
experiencing are due to technical troubles and not to red
tape. You know, the A-4 is rather like a little flower. In order
to flourish, it needs sunshine, a well-proportioned quantity of
fertilizer, and a gentle gardener. What I fear you're planning is a big jet of liquid manure! You know, that might kill
our little flower!"

Von Braun was relieved when Himmler smiled, somewhat
sardonically, at the simile and did not press his offer. After a

few minutes of small talk Himmler dismissed him with no show of hostility but rather with what von Braun could only describe as "feigned politeness." Von Braun flew back to Peenemünde and threw himself into solving the A-4's technical problems. The reasons for the explosions of the rocket on ignition were gradually discovered, and the reports from Blizna became more encouraging.

On the first Sunday in March 1944, von Braun felt the need for a break in his heavy work routine and went to a party at a private house in Zinnowitz, the seaside resort on Usedom Island. Military officers, a few civilians, and many engineers from the Army Experimental Station were present. Von Braun had a few drinks, played the piano in the living room, and then joined Klaus Riedel and Helmut Gröttrup, two of his engineers, for a discussion of the principal topic of conversation during off-duty hours at Peenemünde: developing the rocket for space travel after the war. As for the war itself, von Braun had just learned that his parents had moved to the family estate in Silesia to escape the constant and heavy air raids in Berlin. The war was going very badly at a time when rocket development was improving, and von Braun delivered himself of this opinion. He was, after all, among friends. There were no SS men present, and the brief interview with Himmler had faded from his mind.

Through the hours before dawn of March 15, 1944, General Dornberger lay awake at his new quarters in Schwedt on the Oder River, forty miles south of Peenemünde. He was in a black mood, as black as the bitterly cold Pomeranian night outside his window.

Von Braun and his department heads were giving him trouble. They insisted that the only way to put the A-4 into operation quickly was from fixed concrete pens; the rocket would be wheeled out to static launching sites a few minutes before being fired. Hitler also seemed to be carried away by the concept of giant bunkers. But Dornberger recognized that the Allies now held unchallenged air superiority, had smashed many of the huge firing points already built in northern France, and would discover and smash all fixed targets like these before the concrete had hardened.

Almost alone, Dornberger was fighting for mobility; transporting the A-4 on long trailers to any point desired and having it fired by specially trained motorized military units, who would drive off before they could be detected and attacked from the air. Overcoming resistance to this idea, however, was not the only problem that was keeping Dornberger awake.

Hans Kammler had thrown himself into his job as chief of construction for the A-4 program with a vengeance. Drawing on his experience as director of several concentration camps, he had managed to assign twenty thousand slave laborers to the *Mittelwerke* (Central Works), a vast underground factory in the Harz Mountains that was now producing nearly three hundred A-4's a month. Many of them were faulty, and none were yet ready for anything but training firing crews, but Kammler had gotten action in the production area.

He was, however, obviously not going to stop there. He had annoyed Dornberger by popping up, unannounced and uninvited, to watch the Blizna test firings, chatting in a seemingly offhanded way with Army officers and civilian technicians who were outside his jurisdiction, and "playing one man off against the other." Once he had angered Dornberger by suggesting that von Braun was "too young, too childish, too supercilious and arrogant to be technical director."

Dornberger interpreted all this as the beginning of an SS move to take the rocket program away from the Army. This could only mean disaster. Kammler, who had been an architect in civilian life, knew next to nothing about rockets, which was true of everyone else in the SS Weapons Department.

The telephone jangled on Dornberger's bedside table. He was briefly relieved to have his worries interrupted, but when he learned the origin of the call he experienced a shock: Hitler's headquarters in Berchtesgaden. He was ordered to report at once to a conference with Field Marshal Keitel, Chief of OKW, the Armed Forces High Command.

Dornberger left northern Germany at 8 A.M. He drove over icy roads through snowstorms and then the smoking ruins of Munich, which had been bombed the previous night, and reached Berchtesgaden at dusk. He telephoned General Buhle, chief of the Army staff serving OKW, from his hotel room, and Buhle came hurrying over with the news that Wernher von Braun and the engineers Klaus Riedel and Helmut Gröttrup had been arrested by the Gestapo for sabotage of the A-4 program and taken to the SS jail in Stettin.

"I could not believe my ears," Dornberger described his reaction. "Von Braun, my best man, with whom I had worked in the closest collaboration for over ten years and whom I believed I knew better than anyone, whose whole soul and energy, whose indefatigable toil by day and by night, were devoted to the A-4, arrested for sabotage! It was incredible. And Riedel, who had worked out the entire ground organization with untiring zeal and absolutely outstanding perception of our military needs, who was one of our most devoted followers! And then Gröttrup, Dr. Steinhoff's deputy in guidance and control! Sheer insanity!"

Dornberger demanded to be given the specific reasons for the arrests, but Buhle told him that Field Marshal Keitel himself would do this in the morning. After a "practically sleepless" night Dornberger was ushered into the presence of the senior Army commander in Germany at 9 A.M. Keitel told Dornberger that the charges against the arrested men

were so serious that they were "liable to lose their lives."
When Dornberger said that he was willing to vouch for their
loyalty with his own life, he recalls Keitel replying
"gravely":

"Do you know that your 'closest colleagues' have stated in
company at Zinnowitz that it had never been their intention
to make a weapon of war out of the rocket? That they had
worked, under pressure from yourself, at the whole business of development only in order to obtain money for their
experiments and the confirmation of their theories? That
their object all along has been space travel?"

"Nevertheless, I still vouch for them," Dornberger said. "I
have often said myself in introducing a demonstration at
Peenemünde that our work on the A-4 is only the first tentative step into a new age of technology, that of the rocket.
How often have I insisted that the time is ripe for this
turning-point in human history! We have shown the way to
voyages in space. We have proved that they are possible. If
my men have committed sabotage by repeating such phrases
I ought to be arrested too."

"The sabotage lies in the fact," Dornberger remembers
Keitel telling him, "that these men have given up their
innermost thoughts to space travel and consequently have
not applied their whole energy and ability to production of
the A-4 as a weapon of war."

Dornberger asked where the accusations had come from,
and when Keitel replied that he didn't know, Dornberger
said: "These arrests will be ruinous for the whole project—
especially as the rocket is soon due to come into service and
we haven't even tracked down the latest trouble. There must
be some unfathomable misunderstanding or mistake."

Keitel shrugged his shoulders and said: "I can't do anything about it. Himmler has taken over himself."

So that was it. Himmler had struck at last, in his own in-
imitable fashion. Dornberger persisted in demanding the

release of the three men from Field Marshal Keitel, who was supposed to represent the interests of the Army to the Führer. "Sir, I wish to put on record that if these arrests stand, completion of development will be problematical and employment in the field will have to be postponed indefinitely."

Keitel, however, had clung to his post as Chief of the Armed Forces High Command by the expedient of avoiding clashes with the SS and by not presenting the Führer with ugly problems. He asked Dornberger to be reasonable. "I can't release them without Himmler's agreement," he said. "I must avoid the least suspicion of being less zealous than the secret police and Himmler in these things. You know my position here. I am watched. All my actions are noted. People are only waiting for me to make a mistake. If I ever have to go, the Officers' Corps will have lost the last intermediary between itself and the Führer, its last chance of exercising any influence at all. Then the only rulers will be the Security Service—and Himmler."

Realizing that Keitel was not going to intercede, Dornberger decided on a course of action that few men—in the Germany of 1944—would have undertaken voluntarily. He asked Keitel to arrange an interview for him with Himmler. Keitel put through a call to Berlin and shortly received an answer from Himmler's adjutant. The *Reichsführer SS* refused to see Dornberger. He could, however, present his case to SS General Hans Kaltenbrunner at the SS Security Office.

Field Marshal Keitel, after cautioning General Dornberger to treat their conversation in the strictest confidence, dismissed him. Dornberger drove back to northern Germany in a white heat of rage.

British Intelligence, in March of 1944, was still unable to provide Prime Minister Churchill or the *Crossbow* Committee with any specific details about the German long-range rocket. No solid information had been turned up to indicate when it might be put into action. Not until after the war would intelligence learn that the technical director of Army Experimental Station Peenemünde was not working on the A-4 during the most critical period in its development into an operational weapon.

At three o'clock on the morning of March 13, three Gestapo agents had knocked on the door of Wernher von Braun's bachelor quarters at Peenemünde and asked him to dress quickly and accompany them to the *Polizei Präsidium* in Stettin. Von Braun had protested vigorously, insisting that there must be a misunderstanding. The agents politely but firmly brushed aside his protests; they had clear orders to bring him in for "safekeeping."

At the jail, von Braun was neither threatened nor roughed up. Neither was it explained to him what "safekeeping" meant. "I languished in the SS jail at Stettin for two solid weeks," he later recalled, "without the slightest information from the authorities as to the reasons for my arrest." He found not knowing what was going to happen to him a more unnerving experience than tossing burning rags on primitive, gas-spitting rocket motors had ever been.

The guards came for him at last. He was escorted from his cold cell into what he took to be a small courtroom. He saw, however, no jury or legal counsel and no spectators. The judges, if they were judges, wore no judicial robes, but SS uniforms. They charged von Braun with having said that he had not intended the A-4 to be a weapon, that he had had space travel in mind when developing it, and that he regretted its forthcoming use in action. "That sort of attitude was rather common at Peenemünde," von Braun would recall, "so I felt relatively safe, were that the only accusation they could make against me. But they went further and maintained that I kept an aeroplane in readiness to fly to England with important rocket data. This would be difficult to disprove, for I was in the habit of using a small, government-owned transport plane which I piloted myself on business trips throughout Germany."

The proceedings had an unreal quality which von Braun, as an engineer used to handling tangible problems, found more than a little frightening and insoluble. If the SS was really out to get him for reasons unknown to him, how could he prove that he was not guilty?

It was then that the weirdest incident in this mock trial took place. Major General Dornberger strode into the room, went up to the presiding SS officer, and presented him "with an official-looking document." "No sooner was it read," von Braun recalls, "than my immediate release was ordered and I departed with Dornberger."

The sudden end to the proceedings was the result of two weeks of special pleading by Dornberger. He had gone to the SS Security Office in Berlin (where he was informed that the SS had a "fat file of evidence" against him, too) and then to the Army Counter-Intelligence Department to obtain the release of von Braun, Riedel, and Gröttrup. "My declaration on oath that the arrested men were indispensable to the program had freed them provisionally for three months," Dornberger later observed. "At the end of this time another declaration to the same effect brought a similar adjournment."

This would not, however, be the end of SS designs on the rocket program. Himmler, at the time of von Braun's arrest, was not yet so powerful that he could wrest complete control of the A-4 from the Army, although that time would come. The *Reichsführer SS*, in March 1944, was obliged to employ his usually successful undercover tactics. After von Braun's refusal to join the SS Weapons Department, Himmler started to build a case against the technical director of Army Experimental Station Peenemünde that could be used to convince him that his decision was unwise.

It proved difficult, however, to find anything upon which to build a solid case against an individual like Wernher von Braun. His racial background was formidably "pure" and his political background nonexistent.[5] Gestapo informers sent into Peenemünde could turn up nothing damaging against him until one of them, a woman dentist, overheard von Braun's remarks at the private party in Zinnowitz; taken out of context, they could be made to appear treasonable. Von Braun was hauled up before a court whose purpose was not to find him guilty or innocent but to intimidate him into transferring his talents to the SS. The attempt, largely because of General Dornberger's intervention, had failed, but it had accomplished three things: it created a climate of fear among the civilian technicians assigned to the rocket program; it gave von Braun himself a personal aversion to the Nazis and to all secret-police states; it delayed development of the A-4 as a weapon.

British Intelligence, of course, knew nothing of this complex and tangled web of rivalry surrounding the German secret weapons. Intelligence knew only that the Polish Underground reports continued to indicate that the Germans were testing in southern Poland. When the first Polish reports had come in, Blizna was a thousand flight miles across Germany from Benson, the Oxfordshire base of the Photo Reconnaissance Unit, and beyond the range of its planes. But now, in April, from the new P.R.U. base at San Severo in Italy, Blizna was within range and the weather was clear.

On April 15, 1944, when Wernher von Braun was back at his job as technical director of the A-4 program, a Mosquito took off from San Severo and photographed the suspect Blizna area. The photographs revealed nothing but a huge clearing in the woods and a frustrating camouflage complex. A second flight, on May 5, brought back the same sorts of photographs. On these, however, the photo interpreters detected a single unsettling object: a rocket lying out in the open that allied exactly with those photographed earlier at Peenemünde. The Allied leaders—as D-day approached—were presented with proof that the Germans were continuing with secret weapon development.

Through the month of May the suspected launching sites for the rocket and flying bomb were hit so hard in *Crossbow* air attacks that Air Chief Marshal Sir Roderic Hill judged that most of them "had been rendered unfit for use." But one disconcerting fact remained. Despite the efforts of the photo reconnaissance pilots and the French and Polish Underground agents who risked their lives to provide British Intelligence with information about secret weapons and their launching sites, in the late spring of 1944 "no member of the Allied forces, at any level, knew exactly what the new German weapons might accomplish." [6] This included the man who bore the burden of giving the attack order to the forces assembling for the cross-Channel invasion of occupied France—Dwight Eisenhower.

# 4

## Diver!

On June 4, 1944, General Eisenhower entered the library of Southwick House in southern England. It was 9:30 P.M. He was surrounded by expert advisers, but the decision that had to be made was his alone.

At a morning conference, the weather forecast of low clouds, high winds, and heavy waves had caused Eisenhower to postpone the invasion of France for twenty-four hours. Now he was informed by his chief meteorological officer that a new weather front had been observed. Group Captain Stagg could make no promises, but there was a chance that the weather might clear and hold through the morning of Tuesday, June 6.

Eisenhower polled his twelve senior commanders but found no agreement on what should be done. Montgomery, who would be in charge of ground forces for the assault, voted to go. The respected Deputy Supreme Commander, Air Chief Marshal Tedder, and the Allied Air Commander, Air Chief Marshal Leigh-Mallory, were pessimistic. Considering the circumstances, they viewed the operation as "chancey."

The decision was squarely up to Eisenhower. Watching him, Major General Walter Bedell Smith, his chief of staff, was impressed by "the loneliness and isolation of a commander at a time when such a momentous decision was to be taken by him, with full knowledge that failure or success rests on his individual decision."

Eisenhower weighed the hundreds of problems that had to affect it. Two of them were unknown to the men of the invasion forces and to any but his closest advisers. They both caused him great anxiety.

In late March, a Major A. V. Peterson had been sent to the Supreme Commander by General George C. Marshall upon the strong recommendation of General Leslie Groves, head of the Manhattan Project. Major Peterson informed Eisenhower that the Anglo-Americans were on the track of perfecting a monstrous bomb based on nuclear fission. But Peterson added that the possibility could not be ruled out that the Germans might soon be capable of producing an atom bomb of their own. General Groves considered this chilling possibility remote, but he did want the Supreme Commander warned that the Germans might employ ordinary explosive bombs containing radioactive material, and that they "might lay down some kind of radioactive barrier along the invasion route."

The second problem was more disquieting because it was more tangible. Eisenhower had been thoroughly briefed on the secret weapon threat. He had followed the *Crossbow* air attacks on the launching and supply sites with intense interest. In April he had accorded them priority over all other air operations. He knew that the Anglo-American staff planning *Operation Overlord* had considered in deadly earnest the feasibility of shifting the base of the invasion from the vulnerable ports of southern England to Hull, Glasgow, or Liverpool. After studying all the available evidence on the secret weapons, Lieutenant General Sir Frederick Morgan, the chief *Overlord* planner, had finally delivered himself "painfully of the recommendation that we stay put and take what was to come."

But Eisenhower, despite the strenuous efforts of his intelligence services to provide him with solid facts about the secret weapons, did not really know "what was to come." He did know that southern England was now a vast military camp. Two million men waited in crowded tents, barracks, and Nissen huts. Huge heaps of supplies and munitions had been moved into the assembly areas over jammed roads and railway lines. An armada filled the harbors of Plymouth, Portsmouth, Portland, and Southampton. This teeming arsenal represented the greatest concentration of military power the world had yet seen. It also represented an inviting target for weapons fired from the French coast.

As to what effect the sudden use of secret weapons might have on D-day, Eisenhower "could not even guess." [1] But if—in view of the miserable weather conditions—the risk of giving the order to go was "too chancey," he could guess that an order to postpone D-day to some unknown future date, weeks or possibly months away, was also "too chancey" to be risked. These secret weapons might not be ready now (though he could not be sure of this), but he had to consider the possibility that they would be used very soon, with potentially devastating effect on a concentrated target.

Secret weapons, radioactive materials, the weather—Eisenhower turned all these imponderables over in his mind, along with the hundreds of tangible military problems he could realistically cope with. He narrowed everything down to a simple proposition: "Just how long can you hang this operation at the end of a limb and let it hang there?"

Dwight Eisenhower made his decision: "Okay, we'll go." He called for another meeting early next morning for a last review of the weather forecasts, but now the order went out to the waiting naval armada that the invasion was on. Eisenhower left Southwick House with his senior commanders. In the end, it had taken him 45 seconds to make up his mind to launch the greatest amphibious assault in history.

The next morning, June 5, at 3:30, the Supreme Commander left the big trailer in which he lived and was driven over a mile of rain-lashed, muddy road through winds of almost hurricane force back to Southwick House, where he was told that despite the forbidding storm there was still hope for a break in the weather by June 6. It could last thirty-six hours; beyond that, the meterological experts did not care to predict what would come. Eisenhower pondered this information and then sent a message to the Combined Chiefs of Staff: "Halcyon plus 5 finally and definitely confirmed."

In the murky, gray light of dawn, June 6, men hit the Normandy beaches—Utah, Omaha, Gold, Juno, and Sword. Men of the SS and *Wehrmacht* divisions recovered from their surprise and savagely resisted the steady Allied movement inland. Some of the men on both sides, if they had time to think, may have realized at the close of the day that it was historic, the beginning of the end for Nazi Germany. But none of them could know that it was historic for another reason.

This would be the last D-day. There would, of course, be amphibious assaults in future "limited" wars. But nothing approaching the scale of June 6, 1944, would be seen again because no major conflicts, ever, would be decided by fighting men and conventional weapons. Within the next fifteen months, two new and terrifying weapons—the long-range missile and the atom bomb—would be put into action. Against them, all the armies that had fought over the earth since history began would—massed together—be as powerless as the moles in the bloody fields of Normandy.

None of the soldiers fighting out from the beaches and cliffs toward Carentan, Isigny, St. Lô, and Caen could know this. Nor could they know that Chemical Warfare troops had followed them ashore with Geiger counters but had found no traces of radioactivity. And they could not know that the failure of the secret weapons to attack them had caused great relief to the few Allied leaders who knew of the threat.

By nightfall of June 12, Eisenhower's soldiers had consolidated the rough arc of a bridgehead eight to twelve miles deep and were coiling for the big breakout. *Diver,* the code signal for the appearance of the secret weapons, had still not been flashed. Their failure to reply to the invasion was a source of ironic amusement to those scientific advisers who had maintained from the start of the Sandys investigation that the whole affair was a hoax, a heavy-handed Teutonic joke designed to confuse the Allies into reneging on *Overlord.*

On that night of June 12, however, at 9 P.M., General Alfred Jodl, Chief of Operations of the Armed Forces High Command, sent a message to Colonel Max Wachtel, commanding Flak Regiment 155 (W) in northern France. *Operation Rumpelkammer,* the code name for V-weapon firing, despite its technical shortcomings, had to begin now.

Shortly after 4 A.M., an observer at the Royal Observer Corps in Kent heard a "swishing sound" and saw a miniature airplane passing overhead, orange flames trailing from its exhaust. The observer shouted "Diver!" But it was too late for fighter planes or anti-aircraft guns to intercept the strange object. It flew on, "making a noise like a Model T Ford going up a hill," and dived to earth at Swanscombe at 4:18. Nobody was hurt. Three more of the weird objects struck within the next hour, at Cuckfield, Platt near Sevenoaks, and Bethnal Green. Only in the latter place were there casualties: six dead and nine injured. V-1, the flying bomb, had arrived, and before V-2, the long-range rocket.*

---

* The reasons for this are many and complex, but two principal ones stand out: The Luftwaffe installation at Peenemünde developing V-1 was completely missed in the raid of August 17, 1943, and V-2 was a much more sophisticated scientific instrument, requiring the solution to myriad complicated technical difficulties.

Of the eleven flying bombs which Colonel Wachtel sent screaming off inclined steel rails hidden near Norman farmhouses in the Pas-de-Calais, only these four reached England. Their destructive effect was small but marked the start of the V-weapon attack, and it was clearly not a joke. The British War Cabinet assembled, and meetings were held in Washington to consider ways of dealing with the threat that had become a dismaying actuality and a problem potentially of the first magnitude.

For three days nothing more was heard from Colonel Wachtel's Flak Regiment 155(W). Then, at noon on June 15, a new era in warfare really began. In the next twenty-four hours, 244 V-1's shot from their launch ramps; 144 made it across the Channel; the controls of 77 tripped over London and dived downward, each carrying a ton of explosives. Civilian casualties and property damage were high and alarming. Also alarming was the realization that the Germans were not firing the robots from the kind of massive steel and concrete structures which the British and American Air Forces had gone to such trouble to smash in the *Crossbow* attacks. They had improvised new, smaller, and superbly camouflaged "modified sites" that were difficult to detect.

In the early morning hours of June 16, Winston Churchill called his entire War Cabinet together as the V-1's continued to fall over London. One of the most fateful decisions of the war was made; the long-standing plans to counter the flying bombs were to go into effect immediately, but winning the Battle of France was to remain the primary goal. England would have to take whatever was coming, even if it was far worse than the air raids of 1940-41. General Eisenhower, however, would be asked to see that everything possible was done to destroy the new, modified V-1 launching sites.

Eisenhower acted quickly. On June 16 he sent a memo to his deputy, Air Chief Marshal Tedder:

In order that my desires, expressed verbally at the meeting this morning, may be perfectly clear and of record, with respect to CROSSBOW targets, these targets are to take first priority over everything except the urgent requirements of the battle; this priority to obtain until we can be certain that we have definitely gotten the upper hand of this particular business.[2]

Two battles now raged; the land battle in France and the "Battle of the Flying Bomb." The first went far better than the second. As the troops under his command fought their bloody way deeper into Normandy, Eisenhower and his senior commanders could see the beginning of the end for the determined but crumbling armies facing them. But their optimism was tempered by the knowledge that the rate of V-1 firing was increasing. Beginning at dusk of July 2, 161 flying bombs exploded in the London area in a period of twenty-four hours. And no one knew what would happen if V-2, reportedly a much deadlier missile, was suddenly put into action.

The only certainty about the V-weapons was that if they had been used before D-day the invasion might not have succeeded in opening the second front in France. The man chiefly responsible for the *Overlord* plan, Lieutenant General Sir Frederick Morgan, would later write: "There can be little doubt that had the whole armoury of Hitler's secret weapons come into full play against us we should have been obliged, shall we say, to vary our strategy." Eisenhower would be more specific: "It seemed likely that, if the German had succeeded in perfecting and using these new weapons six months earlier than he did, our invasion of Europe would have proved exceedingly difficult, perhaps impossible. I feel sure that if he had succeeded in using these weapons over a six-month period, and particularly if he had made the Portsmouth-Southampton area one of his principal targets, Overlord might have been written off." [3]

Slowly, however, through the long summer of 1944, the Allies pushed deeper into France and also began to win the "Battle of the Flying Bomb." Allied ground forces overran the V-1 launching sites, and the Air Defence of Great Britain learned to cope with the "nasty little bug."

V-1 traveled at speeds of up to four hundred miles an hour, well below the speed of sound. It could be heard coming, and it could be seen by radar and the human eye. Stripped Spitfire XIV's and Tempests could catch it and either shoot it down or race alongside it, tipping over its wings and sending it to earth before it could reach Greater London. It was a difficult target for the belt of anti-aircraft guns deployed against it, but they too learned to bring it down in increasing numbers.

London suffered through the bombardment of the unmanned planes but survived.[4] V-1 had come too late. It was not going to win the war for Germany or even affect its outcome. That left only V-2 to cast its long dark shadow over the victorious advances of the Allied armies. Nothing had been heard from the long-range rocket, originally regarded as a more imminent threat than the flying bomb, but there was no longer any doubt that it would be used. Intelligence had discovered that it was being mass-produced, and where. Again, aerial reconnaissance provided the answer.

The long, four-finned rockets, so large and unique in design that they were difficult to camouflage, had to be transported along ordinary roads and railway lines from their place of manufacture to their test firing areas. The photo interpreters simply checked these beginning at Blizna and Peenemünde and tracked back to where the rockets had come from. They discovered that hundreds of objects which could only be rockets were originating from Nordhausen, a city in the Harz Mountains.

Plans to bomb the Nordhausen production complex were abandoned when it was discovered that it had been built underground. Instead, the American Eighth Air Force went after the camouflaged but aboveground brain center of the big rocket, where a resumption of activity had been noted. In three daylight raids—July 18 and August 2 and 25—the Eighth dropped nearly two thousand tons of bombs on Peenemünde. But the rockets continued to be shipped in increasing numbers from Nordhausen, and test firing continued at Peenemünde and Blizna.

The Allied leaders, despite all their efforts, were thus still faced with disturbing and unanswered questions about an important obstacle to victory. Intelligence had done a good job in pin-pointing Blizna, Peenemünde, and Nordhausen; the routes used to bring the rockets to their test firing points; the liquid-oxygen plants that supplied their fuel; and in estimating the rocket's appearance and probable potential from ground reports and aerial photographs. But Intelligence had failed to come up with one actual rocket for technical analysis. V-1 was now a known quantity. But V-2, in respect to how it worked, and what destruction it might cause, remained a secret weapon.

Then, in the summer of 1944, after its conventional espionage methods had been frustrated for a year, Intelligence broke the secret.

# 5

## Big Ben

As time ran out for the Third Reich, Peenemünde could no longer afford to maintain the pretense that it had ceased to operate. Camouflage and strict ground security measures remained in force, but test firing had to be openly resumed. On June 13, 1944 (D+7), a peculiar type of missile was set for launching from Test Stand P-7.

Another Peenemünde development was the world's first ground-controlled anti-aircraft rocket, the *Wasserfall* (Waterfall). It had a remote-radio-control guidance system and would be directed to its targets in the air by a ground operator using a joystick control device. The *Wasserfall's* guidance system was ready to be tested in flight. The rocket that would house it, however, was not, so it was decided to use an A-4 as a test carrier.

The A-4 was not remote-radio-controlled, but for test purposes one could be fitted up with *Wasserfall* guidance elements. Three hundred pounds of burning alcohol and liquid oxygen flamed and smashed over the launch table of Test Stand P-7 as an A-4 carrying *Wasserfall* instruments lifted and streaked into a blue sky, responding as planned to ground controls. Eventually it would be sent plunging into the Baltic, its impact point marked for the search teams by the bags of green dye it carried to stain the surface of the sea.

But the ground engineer who was maneuvering the control system in this A-4 for the first time in flight suddenly lost the rocket at 6,000 feet as a heavy bank of clouds drifted into his line of sight. Momentarily panicked, thinking that it might swing south and fall on some German coastal town, he steered it northward over the Baltic Sea. Apart from this improvisation, the test flight seemed successful. The search teams, however, speeding out in their motorboats, failed to locate the spreading green circles of dye.

Wernher von Braun insisted on knowing exactly where every test missile impacted. He was not satisfied to be told in this instance that "it slipped off course but undoubtedly sank in the north Baltic." He directed his Guidance and Control Branch to make a thorough check. Twenty-four hours later, after an evaluation of the Doppler tracking records, Guidance and Control came back with an unsettling conjecture: the missile might have landed in southern Sweden.

Major General Dornberger was at Blizna when this test shot took place, and it was there that he received a telephone call from Wolf's Lair, Hitler's headquarters in East Prussia. Had any missiles been launched from Peenemünde recently? Dornberger telephoned the Experimental Station and was told that neither an A-4 nor an Fi-103 (V-1) had been launched. This answer did not satisfy headquarters. Something resembling an A-4 was reported to have broken up in an airburst over southern Sweden and its fragments had fallen near the town of Kalmar. The Swedish Government was raising "a hell of a row" and had protested to the Führer himself.

Dornberger telephoned Peenemünde again and this time learned the details of the test shot, including von Braun's opinion that it must have impacted in Sweden. Dornberger reported this to Hitler's headquarters and was asked if the fragments of the fallen A-4 could be pieced together to give any indication of the way it worked. He had to answer yes. But when asked if a replica would enable to the Allies to use radio interference, he answered no. "I felt confident enough," Dornberger recalls, "to add the assurance that the *Wasserfall* control equipment would give the enemy's intelligence service some hard nuts to crack and might lead to false conclusions."

Dornberger was then ordered to Wolf's Lair "to receive a reprimand, with the consoling comment that Hitler was in a towering rage." But when he arrived he was told that the Führer did not want to see him, after all. "Hitler had declared," Dornberger recalled, "that it was quite a good thing for the Swedes to realize that we could bombard their country from Germany; they would be more inclined to be cooperative in negotiations."

The neutral Swedes, however, did not react in quite that way to a German rocket hitting their country. The Swedish Government was not co-operative about turning over the rocket fragments it had collected to the German Embassy in Stockholm; repeated requests to do so were flatly refused. The Germans realized that the wreckage was more revealing than the layman might suppose, because the pieces of a rocket that breaks up at a high altitude—as this one had—are slowed by air resistance and "flutter" to earth without suffering much additional damage in the final crash.

British agents in Sweden quickly learned of the "Kalmar Specimen." When British Intelligence suggested that it would appreciate being given the parts of an object it had been trying to find since April 1943, the Swedes did not say no.

Lieutenant Colonel Keith N. Allen was permitted to fly an unarmed C-47 cargo plane of the American Transport Command into neutral Sweden. Huge unmarked crates were loaded into the C-47. Once beyond Sweden, Allen was met by a heavy fighter escort and flew back to England. The crates were unpacked, and Allied scientists, like archaeologists reconstructing a Greek temple from fragments of columns and cornices, reassembled and analyzed for the first time a fair representation of Germany's most closely guarded secret.

One thing about the reconstructed rocket, however, did lead the Anglo-American scientists to "false conclusions." From the remains of the *Wasserfall* remote-radio-control guidance system found in the wreckage flown in from Sweden, they assumed that all V-2's would have such a guidance system. This gave hope that the rocket in flight could be diverted from its targets by jamming the radio. Later it would be discovered that this was a false hope.[1] But as of the first week in July, the "Kalmar Specimen" had revealed so much interesting, and disturbing, information that the scientists pressed Intelligence to provide them with another rocket for analysis, preferably one in better condition.

Although the "Swedish incident" was not repeated, Intelligence filled the request.

In that hot July of 1944, although the field performance of the A-4 was improving, many of them were still breaking up in the air about two miles before impact. Dornberger suggested to von Braun that he go to southern Poland and "establish headquarters at the exact bullseye of the target area."

This solution to pin-pointing the A-4's technical shortcomings was not as grim as it sounded. No A-4 had yet come within two miles of striking a planned land target. "It was Dornberger's reasoning," von Braun recalled, "that dead center of the target area would certainly be the safest spot." All this changed, however. One day von Braun was standing in an open field looking at a time indicator atop an observation tower which announced when a rocket fired from

Blizna, two hundred miles away, was due to arrive. When the time indicator showed that a rocket was coming into the area, von Braun glanced in the direction from which it was expected and saw a thin contrail streaking across the sky. To his "horror," he saw that it was heading right toward him.

"There was barely time to fall on the ground before I was hurled high in the air by a thunderous explosion, to land unhurt in a nearby ditch," von Braun recalls. "The impact had taken place three hundred yards away and it was a miracle that the exploding warhead did not grind me into powder."

The A-4 was improving in accuracy. But von Braun and his crew of evaluators were not alone in observing the improvement from close range. The Polish Underground was watching too. Ever since the Poles had reported the construction of the Blizna range, they had followed the instructions of British Intelligence to find out all they could about what was going on in the area.

The Poles had reported much that was helpful, especially about the V-1 flying bomb that was also tested at Blizna. But the urgent request to capture a long-range rocket, kidnap a German rocket expert, or even to find rocket fragments that had fallen off course proved to be beyond the resources of the Polish Underground. It lacked weapons and mobility. The able-bodied men who had escaped German prisoner-of-war camps, forced-labor battalions, or death were few in number. And those few were now heavily engaged in *Burza* (Storm), the partisan warfare campaign ordered by the Polish Government-in-Exile in London as the Red Army approached the borders of eastern Poland.

Nevertheless, some Underground units patrolled the line of fire of the rockets in southern Poland and noted the reports of the peasants living there. The Underground was informed of each rocket impact. But it was no match for the

German motorized patrols which arrived to collect all the fragments, then drove off, leaving empty craters behind. For months the Poles—lacking the fire and manpower to engage the Germans—watched helplessly as their desperately sought-after prize was driven away.

Then late one afternoon an off-course A-4 hurtled into the sandy bank of the Bug River near the village of Sarnaki in the Warsaw District. Its warhead failed to explode. A German motorized unit was sent speeding toward the Sarnaki area. But this time a Polish patrol happened to be passing through and got there first. The Poles saw that the rocket was intact, but they had neither the means nor the time to make off with it before the Germans arrived. It was the most frustrating moment since the search had begun in January 1944.

Then one of the Poles had an idea. Twenty Underground men strained at the rocket's side and managed to roll it off the bank into the shallow Bug River. It could still be seen, however, in the clear blue water. In a nearby field, a herd of cows graced peacefully. The Poles dashed into the herd and drove the cows into the river. Five minutes later the German search party arrived and saw only a herd of cows watering in a river. The cows had churned its clear blue surface into a thick, muddy brown. The Germans drove off in another direction in search of the elusive rocket.

The Poles returned at nightfall with tools, three battered trucks, and a team of Underground engineers. The rocket was hauled out of the water and dismantled by the light of flaming torches veiled by blankets. The unexploded warhead presented a dangerous problem. It appeared to contain about a ton of high-explosive Amatol. But the Poles went to work, knowing that the slightest miscalculation could blow them to bits, and defused it. Just before dawn the three trucks moved off with a precious cargo.

British Intelligence was radioed that the Polish Underground was at last in possession of a German long-range rocket. It was in almost perfect condition. Intelligence replied that it wanted the rocket in England at all costs. How a twelve-ton, forty-six-foot-long rocket could be gotten out of an occupied, embattled Poland to the Royal Aircraft Establishment at Farnborough was a question that baffled the Polish Underground, but London advised that a solution was being worked on.

Intelligence finally came up with a plan that might work, if all the factors involved meshed perfectly. The R.A.F. base at Brindisi, Italy, was only six hundred flight miles from Poland. The R.A.F. had already sent one stripped bomber to an abandoned German airfield in Poland with a cargo of guerrilla weapons and supplies. In a space of ten minutes the bomber had landed, unloaded, and taken off for Brindisi, completely escaping the attentions of the Luftwaffe. This small airfield, with the Polish code name of *Motyl* (Butterfly), was chosen by Intelligence as the collection point for the long-range rocket. The pickup, London radioed the Poles, would have to be timed to take no more than twenty minutes. After that, the Germans would certainly realize that something was going on and close in on *Motyl*.

The Poles agreed but wondered what type of bomber could carry a twelve-ton rocket. The complete rocket was not necessary, London replied; only its essential parts were needed, supplemented by accurate technical drawings of the whole object. For three weeks a Polish Underground engineer and aircraft designer, A. Kocjan, drew the blueprints while other engineers selected and boxed what they considered essential parts.

On the morning of July 25, 1944, British Intelligence radioed the Poles that the pickup would be that night. In a heavy rain the Poles brought the boxes close to *Motyl*, and four hundred Underground fighters armed with old rifles and carbines staked out positions in the woods surrounding the airfield. They knew that a Luftwaffe ground detachment, four hundred strong, was stationed a mile distant and that a German cavalry squadron was quartered in a village two miles away.

At four-thirty in the quiet afternoon the rain stopped and the waiting Poles were stunned to see a German fighter land on the rutted, soggy surface of what was thought to be an abandoned airstrip. Five minutes later a second German fighter landed as a radio message was received that an R.A.F. Dakota was on its way from Brindisi. The planes sat there until dusk. Then they took off as suddenly as they had come. The Poles decided with relief that they had been on routine training flights.

The dark summer night was fair and quiet. The only sound was the faint rumble of artillery fire from the Russian July offensive to the east. Toward midnight the Poles heard the engines of an approaching plane. They dashed to the boundaries of the airstrip, fired torches to guide the bomber in, and placed an arrow of red lights in the center of the airstrip to indicate wind direction. The Dakota made three passes, then roared in to a perfect landing. Kocjan got aboard with 110 pounds of key rocket parts and the technical drawings. The operation had taken ten minutes. The Dakota's engines, which had been kept running, were gunned for the take-off.

But the big bomber did not respond. Its tires had become bogged down in the rain-soaked surface of the airstrip. As the seconds passed, the twenty-minute limit set for the operation became a grim joke. The Dakota, its powerful engines opened to full boost and booming through the quiet night, vibrated helplessly on the ground. After almost an hour had passed since landing, the pilot suggested that the rocket parts be unloaded, hidden again, and the plane burned.

But the Poles persisted. They ran to the neighboring village and returned with shovels and other tools and materials. They dug narrow, gently sloping trenches in front of the Dakota's wheels and filled the trenches with straw and wooden planks. An hour and a half after it had landed, the Dakota moved forward, gained speed, and lumbered off the ground to clear the trees and roar off into the sky. "We of the Underground," one eyewitness later recalled, "melt into the darkness of the woods." Another eyewitness has commented, "The Germans close at hand, almost within hailing distance, were either too tired by their strenuous marches to care for what went on around them or did not want to risk their skins in an armed encounter with the Home Army. . . . They gave no sign of life during the whole operation, by which a military secret of the first importance was transferred to their enemies under their very noses."

The Dakota was not attacked by the Luftwaffe as it returned to Brindisi, from where Kocjan, his blueprints and rocket parts were flown to England. As the only technician on the Allied side who had ever seen and studied an almost intact German long-range rocket, he was interrogated round the clock for a week at the Royal Aircraft Establishment at Farnborough. Then he was told that he could remain in England, but he insisted upon returning to his homeland; there was still work to be done in Poland.

"The gallant man, Mr. A. Kocjan," Winston Churchill wrote, "returned to Poland, and was later caught by the Gestapo and executed in Warsaw on August 13, 1944." [2]

The information that Kocjan had supplied, however, together with the "Kalmar Specimen," permitted the Allied leaders to know by the end of August, according to Churchill, "exactly what to expect" from Big Ben, the code name now assigned to the long-range rocket by British Intelligence.

The top-secret *Project Big Ben,* which was charged with reconstructing and evaluating the captured missiles, was directed by the British rocket expert, Sir Alwyn Crow. His team, however, was not completely British. The Americans had begun to take an interest in Big Ben, and representatives of the technical branches of the American armed forces were assigned to Farnborough. One of them, Lieutenant Commander Thomas F. Dixon, was sent to England by the U.S. Navy Bureau of Ordnance. Dixon found the unlocking of the technical secrets of the Big Bens to be "very simple."

"We had parts of the nose section, turbo-pumps, thrust chambers," he later recalled. "From these we made a scientific study of what the rocket could deliver in terms of thrust, durability, and range. In a matter of two weeks we had the specifications figured." [3]

Von Braun himself would later acknowledge that "the British Intelligence team did a remarkable job in piecing together an accurate picture of the V-2 and all its components." The picture was alarming. Big Ben was obviously something new and hair-raising in the history of warfare. It weighed about twelve tons, was about forty-six feet long and five feet in diameter, carried a warhead of approximately a ton of high explosives, and had a range of at least 210 miles, which meant that it could easily reach Greater London from the French or Dutch coasts. It was not, after all, controlled by radio from the ground, but by internal gyroscopes which could not be jammed. Unlike V-1, V-2 was supersonic, which meant what it would approach unseen and unheard and that there was no way to stop it once it had been launched. Dr. R. V. Jones, Chief of the Scientific Intelligence Branch of the Air Ministry, informed Mr. Churchill "that there might well be a thousand rockets already in existence." [4]

This disturbing picture had a bright side, however. Aerial reconnaissance had discovered no fixed sites from which it was believed that a rocket of this size would have to be fired. And even if such launching sites existed, the Allied armies were close to pushing the Germans back beyond the 210-mile firing range of the V-2. There appeared to be a very good chance that Big Ben, after all the anxiety and effort it had caused, would never be used in action. But the most optimistic of the *Project Big Ben* evaluators conceded that there was only one man who could really say whether "Hitler's rocket" would be fired against England: Adolf Hitler himself.

# A heavy body rushing through the air

On July 20, 1944, Hitler narrowly survived the explosion of the time bomb placed under the conference table in his East Prussian headquarters by Colonel Klaus Schenk, Count von Stauffenberg. Because the plot against his life had been taken part in by high-ranking Army officers, Hitler's lack of confidence in his generals turned into contemptuous hatred.

Himmler and the trusted SS became the dominant power in the Third Reich. One of the many side effects of this was the removal of all obstacles to Himmler's long-standing desire to take over the A-4. In an irony that would escape Allied Intelligence until the war's end, "Hitler's rocket" had not been ready for action well before D-day primarily because Hitler himself had delayed its development.*

---

* Hitler never visited Peenemünde. As noted in Chapter Two, he personally canceled Peenemünde's urgently needed top priority in the spring of 1940 and refused to restore it as late as March 1943 because "I have dreamed that the rocket will never be operational against England. I can rely on my inspirations. It is therefore pointless to give further support to this project." This pronouncement was relayed to Dornberger by Albert Speer, the Nazi Minister of Munitions, and Dornberger later saw it in a memorandum at the ministry. In July 1943, Hitler finally threw his support and the full technical resources of the Third Reich into the A-4 program. Had he done so in 1940 there can be little doubt that thousands of rockets would have been ready for use at least six

Now the Führer was demanding its early use and raging that London be blown off the map. Himmler moved quickly to implement the Führer's wishes.

On August 1, 1944, he appointed Dr. Hans Kammler, who had been quickly advanced from the rank of SS brigadier general to major general, as Special Commissioner for the A-4 program. Until this appointment, Kammler, as chief of the building branch of the SS Main Office, had been responsible only for the construction work required by the A-4 project. Now he was given full power over everything from development to firing. "My orders and his directions are to be obeyed," read the order which Himmler signed personally.

Major General Dornberger's struggle to retain control of the Army rocket program which he had begun in 1930 was over. He was shocked and depressed by the appointment of Kammler, who, he knew, had only the most superficial understanding of rocketry. Only a month before, Kammler had told Dornberger that he should be court-martialed for wasting so much money and manpower in trying to make a reality out of a fantasy like the long-range rocket.

"I felt like a man," Dornberger described his reaction to Kammler's appointment as Special Commissioner, "who has devoted years of toil and affection to making a superb violin, a masterpiece which needs only tuning, and who then has to look on helplessly while the instrument is grabbed by a tough, unmusical woodsman and scraped like a jagged lump of wood."

SS General Kammler was in his late forties. His dark hair was touched with gray streaks, and his brown eyes were piercing and restless. He struck Dornberger as looking "like some hero of the Renaissance, a *condottiere* . . . with a lean,

---

months before D-day, with consequences upon which it is interesting to speculate. All of the Allied efforts combined were not as effective in delaying the use of "Hitler's rocket" as Hitler himself.

curved beak of a nose, and a strong mouth, the underlip thrust forward as though in defiance. That mouth indicated brutality, derision, disdain and overweening pride. . . ."

Dornberger's first impression of Kammler had been of a "virile, handsome and captivating personality." His second impression, concurred in by von Braun, was that Kammler was an energetic opportunist who lacked the technical background to direct the rocket program. On one day alone, Dornberger received 123 teletype orders from Kammler, scores of them contradictory, most of them meaningless from the viewpoint of accomplishing anything technically useful. Dornberger seriously considered resigning from the A-4 program but was persuaded to stay on by von Braun and Ernst Steinhoff. Dornberger remained as Kammler's "technical staff officer." By controlling his temper and offering ideas to Kammler as though the Special Commissioner had originated them himself, Dornberger hung on in a position where he could further the progress of the A-4 toward its use against the enemy.

Hans Kammler spent the last week in August 1944 inspecting the *Mittelwerke* (Central Works) in the village of Niedersachswerfen, two and a half miles from the city of Nordhausen.

To inspect the *Mittelwerke*, Kammler had to go underground. Two parallel tunnels,[1] each slightly more than a mile long, had been driven under the soft rock of a slope of the Harz, Germany's northernmost mountain range. Forty-seven smaller cross tunnels, where the machining and subassembly of parts were done, connected the two main tunnels, which served as the assembly and transportation points. The network of tunnels was illuminated by overhead lamps and ventilated by large metal ducts bringing in forced drafts of temperature-controlled air.

Railroad tracks led into the two main tunnels, where the Junkers aero-engines assembled in one half of the underground factory and the V-1's and V-2's assembled in the other could be loaded without detection from outside. The *Mittelwerke* operated twenty-four hours a day, seven days a week. Because of its "practically bombproof situation," the Allied Air Forces never attempted a direct attack on it.

Hans Kammler and the SS ruled this underground kingdom. German experts from Peenemünde, the universities, and private industry directed production, assisted by some three thousand German technicians. The heavy labor was done by non-Germans. Kammler supplied the *Mittelwerke* with six thousand slave laborers from the nearby Nordhausen and Dora concentration camps and from Buchenwald, forty miles away.

During August, Kammler noted on his inspection tour, the *Mittelwerke* had assembled 265 long-range rockets, making a total of over a thousand since production had begun. Dornberger and von Braun had told him that these missiles had flaws and needed refinements before they could be expected to be used operationally. Kammler brushed aside this counsel of Germany's two leading rocket experts. A-4 had to be put into action at once. He ordered assembled rockets moved to the western front. Then he flew to Brussels and informed the Chief of Staff of the XV Army Corps, which was responsible for V-weapon firing, of his decision.

A slim booklet, stamped "Top Secret," was distributed in late August 1944 to the troops assigned to fire the long-range rocket. It was a technical manual, called *A-4 Fibel* (Primer), and its authors had gone to some pains to simplify its instructions, which were imparted through short sentences, little homilies, and stanzas of jaunty verse. The primer was enlivened with cartoons of bosomy girls attired in bathing suits and negligees and drawings of German villages covered with Christmas snow. The first chapter set the tone:

LISTEN EVERYBODY!
Here, dear Reader, is
the new A-4 primer.
This dry material is presented
in an easy manner
So that it will become part
of your flesh and blood.
However, always remember one thing

ALL THIS MATERIAL ABOUT THE A-4
IS TOP SECRET. REMEMBER THAT!
. . . on this planet where you live
In an age of guided missiles
A sky ship in the universe—
A long dream of mankind—
May someday fascinate our century.
But today you must master a weapon still
Unknown because it is classified top secret.
It is called, for short, the A-4 Device. . . .
Whoever talks about it commits treason
and damages himself and the State.
First of all, remember, do not enter
into any debate.
Should an outsider, an informer or
a wise-guy question you
Tell him with a stupid expression on your face
I don't know anything.

YOU ARE A MEMBER OF THE LONG-RANGE
ROCKET SQUAD.
You will help launch the A-4. You will work with a projectile that flies higher and farther than any known projectile. The A-4 has a detonation effect unequaled until now by any missile or bomb. . . .

FASTER THAN SOUND
*Only five minutes will elapse between launching and impact.* In those five minutes, however, everything must operate perfectly. Every single element of the A-4 has to be tested carefully and set prior to launching to insure that the missile hits its target. Little things may cause misfiring. . . .

**[A heavy body rushing through the air]**

REMEMBER:
Every miss will help the enemy, damage us through the loss
of valuable materials, and endanger the lives of you and
your comrades.

MORAL:
The A-4 will hold it against you if you don't study this
manual carefully. If you do, the enemy will be troubled by
each of your well-placed shots.[2]

The little primer was studied intently by firing crews
hidden in the thick woods of the Haagsche Bosch just outside
The Hague. They were less than two hundred miles from
London. It was the first week of September 1944.

The military situation confronting Adolf Hitler at this
time had grown desperate. In Italy, Rome and Mussolini had
fallen. Paris had been liberated, and the Allied armies had
cleared northern France, most of Belgium and Luxembourg,
and reached the Rhine borders of Germany itself. Cities and
factories from one end of Germany to the other were being
pounded by armadas of heavy bombers.

On the eastern front, the Russian summer offensive had
steam-rollered into Rumania and Bulgaria and was heading
for the Hungarian border and Vienna. The Red Army swept
into Poland and paused on the outskirts of Warsaw as the
Polish Underground began an uprising in the battered city.

Hitler now looked like an old man. The tympanic mem-
branes of his ears, which had been broken in the bomb explosion of July 20, caused him great irritation. He suffered
from stomach cramps and continual headaches. His voice was
weak, his face ashen, and his hands shook.

Yet Hitler drove himself on. He retained complete control
of operations. As the military situation continued to disinte-
grate, he began to talk increasingly of how it would be suddenly and dramatically changed by the new weapons German
science had created. The new electric-powered U-boats would

clear the seas; the new jet fighters would clear the skies; the new V-weapons would change the course of the war at the eleventh hour. On June 14 he had briefly visited the front in Normandy and assured his generals that the flying bomb "would be decisive against Great Britain . . . and make the British willing to make peace." [3]

But it had not been decisive. The V-1 bombardment reached its climax in July and August and then petered out as the launching sites in northern France were overrun by Allied troops. Allied fears about a large-scale attack by "Hitler's rocket" began to dwindle. The Germans had been driven from all areas within the 200-mile range of the V-2 from London, except for Holland. And in Holland aerial reconnaissance still found no large launching sites for rockets.

The danger which had caused the insiders such anxiety since the first report of the Sandys investigation appeared to be over. On September 1, British civil defense stopped its planning of precautionary measures in the event of rocket attack. On September 6, the British Chiefs of Staff, concluding that "there should shortly be no further danger," agreed that all *Crossbow* air attacks on suspected rocket transportation systems and storage depots could be halted. On September 7, Duncan Sandys, as chairman of the Flying Bomb Counter-Measures Committee, held a press conference in London. For the first time, the public was given a concise summary of the V-1, from the time its existence was discovered through its defeat.

"The visitation which London has so bravely endured has been painful enough," Sandys observed. "Had it not been for the vigilance of our Intelligence services, the unrelenting efforts of the British and American Air Forces, and the effectiveness of the defenses, London's ordeal might well have been many times more severe."

Sandys did not mention V-2 until a reporter asked him about it as the close of the conference. "I am a little chary of talking about V-2," Sandys said. "We do know quite a lot about it. In a very few days' time I feel that the press will be walking all over these places in France, and will know a great deal more than we do now."

But in his opening sentence to the press, Sandys had committed himself to a prediction: "Except possibly for a few last shots, the Battle of London is over." [4]


The next evening, September 8, 1944, at 6:43 P.M., residents of the London suburb of Chiswick who were returning home from work or already sitting down to dinner were startled by "a sharp report which sounded almost, but not quite, like a peal of thunder," immediately followed by the sound of a heavy body rushing through the air. Twenty houses were shattered, three people killed, and ten seriously injured. Sixteen seconds later, the same weird explosion occurred at Parndon Wood, near Epping. It demolished some wooden huts but did no other damage. [5]

The local residents were baffled by the cause of the explosions; no German bombers or V-1's had been seen or heard anywhere near the impact areas. The scientific intelligence teams which rushed to Chiswick and Epping, however, immediately realized what had happened. The "Battle of London" was not over. One of the two most feared new weapons of World War II (the other, of course, the atom bomb) had at last been put into action. To confirm that V-2 had arrived, the intelligence teams had only to listen to descriptions of the explosions. V-2, they knew, traveled beyond the speed of sound. The explosion would be heard first, followed by the sound of the rocket's approach, the "heavy body rushing through the air."

There was no press statement about what had happened at Chiswick and Epping. The British Government, in fact, withheld the official announcement about the V-2 for another two months, until it could gauge the rocket's effect on civilian morale. During those two months, two hundred of the strange explosions occurred in southern England, mostly within Greater London.

As anticipated, there was no way to stop V-2 once it had been launched. Until Allied troops could push the last of the Germans beyond the rocket's firing range, London would just have to take it, again. And the first city ever to be subjected to guided missile attack took it well.

Both the blitz of the grim winter of 1940-41 and the V-1 bombardment seemed, curiously enough, more harrowing experiences. One could see the V-1, hear it rattling overhead like a flying trolley car, hear the sudden cutoff of its motor and know that this would send it diving earthward. The roaring Luftwaffe bombers and the buzzing V-1's gave nerve-wracking warning of their approach.

There was no long, tense, anxious wait to discover what V-2 would do. One could be at home reading *The Times* or making love to one's wife, shopping at the Woolworth store in Deptford or having a pint of bitter at the Rose and Crown, and suddenly, without warning, the earth would shake and fly apart. Those who survived on the fringes of a V-2 blast would never forget its sounds. First, there was a whiplike crack as the missile, moving faster than sound, created a compression wave which bounced from the point of impact and struck the ear a split second before the brilliant white flash of the exploding warhead. Then came a gale of rubble and shattered glass and the slower sound of V-2's arrival, an ear-filling roar which diminished gradually and finally lost itself in the sky.

And yet this was all very impersonal. Whether one lived or died was soon seen to be a matter of pure chance. One could be young or old, brave or cowardly, a charwoman or a Cabinet minister, and it made not the slightest difference. Since there was nothing anyone could do about V-2, there seemed no point in worrying about it unduly; the response to it was almost fatalistic.

As the rocket attacks mounted in intensity (sixty-three fell in the fortnight ending November 4) the Allied authorities took the only countermeasure possible. Strenuous efforts were made to alleviate London's ordeal by pin-pointing the V-2 launching sites through aerial reconnaissance and then bombing them out of action. It was quickly discovered that most of the rockets were coming from the Haagsche Bosch, the main park of The Hague. Allied reconnaissance flights followed by bombing attacks failed, however, to stop the rockets from roaring up out of the woods.

The reason for this failure was simple. The reconnaissance planes had never been able to detect any of the large fixed sites that were believed necessary for firing the V-2 because none was needed. General Dornberger had won his fight for mobility. The V-2's could be driven anywhere on their *Meillerwagen* (long road trailer), quickly set up on their four fins, fueled, and fired. A road crossing, an aircraft runway, or any hard, level surface could serve as a launch platform. The mobile crews took up any position they chose under the thick, sheltering trees of the Haagsche Bosch, fired, and drove away. Some V-2's were destroyed by bombing en route from the *Mittelwerke* to Holland, but not one, according to von Braun, was ever hit at a mobile launch site.

Von Braun and Dornberger had been right, however, in maintaining that the A-4 was not ready for mass production and operational use. The failures under actual firing conditions were almost eight percent, as Dr. Kooy and Professor Uytenbogaart, Dutch scientists who observed the rockets rising above The Hague, reported to Allied Intelligence. Some blew up on their pads and killed their crews, others failed to work at all, and others that did get off the ground fell short into the North Sea.

The British and American leaders came to realize that V-2, while a spectacular technical achievement, had fortunately appeared too late and in too few numbers to have any effect on the war.[6] There was, despite bombing attacks on The Hague and other suspect launching areas on the Dutch coast, a steady increase in the number of incidents, "that non-committal word used to describe the sudden and violent disintegration of buildings and the persons in them," [7] as the official R.A.F. history would later put it. One obvious fact, however, stood out. After the long anxiety about V-2, this first guided missile—when it finally appeared—turned out for all practical purposes to be a military failure.

Allied troops destroyed the transportation systems bringing the rocket from Nordhausen to Holland, captured the plants supplying it with fuel, and finally drove the firing crews out of Holland. On March 27, 1945, a V-2 landed in Kynaston Road, Orpington, Kent. It was the last "incident." As the Allied armies went on to break the Third Reich in a giant pincer, V-2 was forgotten, or if remembered at all, remembered as a brief, terrifying footnote to World War II. The V-2 story appeared to have ended on March 27 in Kent.

There was a handful of technical experts in England, the United States, and the Soviet Union who did not, however, dismiss V-2 as a passing phenomenon or a spectacular failure. They realized that it had changed the nature of future wars and that their own countries had no rockets that could begin to compare with V-2 in size, destructiveness, and sophistication of engineering.

The technical experts urged the intelligence services of their respective countries to go into Germany when it was defeated to find the German rocket specialists and the V-2 technical documents. V-2, no longer a threat and the target of a secret weapon investigation, became the target of another kind of search, one in which the British began with a distinct advantage. The Americans, who had assisted in

*Crossbow* and *Project Big Ben,* followed the clear British lead. The Russians were far behind their Allies.

Soviet Intelligence, however, had given evidence that it, too, was after a prize of war that could lead to intercontinental ballistic missiles and the exploration of outer space. In July 1944, Soviet Intelligence had armed German prisoners of war with money, false documents, and short-wave radios and parachuted them around Peenemünde. But only a Lieutenant Brandt played the game and radioed back anything of interest, and he was caught by *Funk Abwehr* (Radio Intelligence) after his seventh message and executed.[8]

In August 1944, the Red Army had captured the Blizna firing range. On September 3, the Russians permitted a team of British and American rocket experts to inspect the Polish site. Blizna, however, had been evacuated by the Germans and yielded no important information. But as winter approached, Soviet Intelligence, still behind the British and Americans, kept its patience. It had reason to believe that the Anglo-American lead would eventually be overcome and that the Soviet Union would gain full possession of the V-2 spoils of war.

# 7

## Decision

In January 1945, the Red Army launched its greatest offensive of the war. One hundred and eighty divisions attacked in East Prussia and Poland alone. Warsaw fell on January 17. Panzer General Heinz Guderian, the then new Chief of the Army General Staff, noted: "By January 27 the Russian tidal wave was rapidly assuming for us the proportions of disaster." [1] That same day the tidal wave, breaking over East Prussia, rolled to within a hundred miles of Berlin and also Peenemünde.

As early as the spring of 1943, Wernher von Braun had realized that Germany could not win the war and that the V-2 would not be a "miracle weapon" that would alter the military situation. He learned through a newspaper account that it had been put into action. An associate recalls him "realistically" telling an excited group of engineers in his Peenemünde office: "Let's not forget that this is only the beginning of a new era, the era of rocket-powered flight. It seems that this is another demonstration of the sad fact that so often important new developments get nowhere until they are first applied as weapons." [2]

V-2 had indeed not turned out to be the *Wunderwaffe*—miracle weapon—heralded by Goebbels' Propaganda Ministry. By January 27, 1945, von Braun realized not only that the war was definitely lost but that there was no obstacle to the Russians inevitably engulfing the rocket center. He would switch on the radio and hear the confident voice of a German newscaster announcing that the front had been stabilized. Before the German newscaster could finish, the Russians would break in with a beamed transmitter and announce: "Propaganda! Lies! Today the Red Army broke through at . . ."

Von Braun saw the hordes of frightened refugees from East Prussia fleeing westward across Pomerania, among them the bent old people pushing wheelbarrows piled high with their belongings and hungry young mothers trudging through the snow with half-frozen babies strapped to their backs. He walked through the bomb-scarred streets of Peenemünde and watched civilian engineers being instructed in close-order drill and the use of the rifle and bayonet. Peenemünde, it appeared, was going to be defended against the oncoming Red Army, although it was of no strategic or tactical importance. Moreover, such a futile defense could only result in the destruction of the great rocket center. On the other hand, if Peenemünde was not defended and was left to fall easily to the Red Army, the Soviet Union would come into possession there of the A-4, the technical documents, the test stands, research buildings, and five thousand technicians with unique skills in a brand-new technology. At one stroke the Russians would gain an unbeatable lead in the coming age of guided missiles and, if they decided to pursue the non-military application of the rocket, an unbeatable lead in future space exploration.

Von Braun felt that he knew how to solve this dilemma. At thirty-two, he was the man to whom everyone at Peenemünde looked for decisions. With Himmler's appointment of Hans Kammler as Special Commissioner in August, Dornberger had been assigned an additional duty and was now at the Ministry of Munitions in Berlin, leading a group of technical experts charged with developing weapons to "break enemy air superiority." At Peenemünde itself, von Braun, a civilian with no authority over the military actions of the Army or the SS, could not order the one step which, in his estimation, could save the rocket station from the advancing Russians: evacuation of its leading personnel and key equipment to the west.

After the R.A.F. raid of August 17, 1943, Army Experimental Station Peenemünde had had its name changed to *Heimat Artillerie Park* (Home Artillery Park). In the summer of 1944, in the hope of further misleading Allied Intelligence and to increase operating efficiency, HAP was transformed into a civilian, state-owned industrial concern labeled EW—*Elektromechanische Werke* (Electromechanical Works), Karlshagen, Pomerania. Paul Storch of Siemens, Germany's biggest private electric company, was appointed general manager of EW. But Storch was, in General Dornberger's restrained phrase, "a stranger to our work." Storch, a man of ability and tact, realized his limitations in the field of rocketry. When the commanding personality of Dornberger was removed by the SS, Storch deferred to von Braun. Kammler and the SS, however, retained final control over Peenemünde, and they showed no intention of evacuating it, even when faced by a hopeless situation. In fact, several EW engineers who had talked openly of the need for abandoning Peenemünde had been arrested by the SS, shot, and their corpses hung from trees along well-traveled avenues, bearing placards reading: I WAS TOO COWARDLY TO DEFEND THE HOMELAND.

But then on January 31, 1945, a bitterly cold day when von Braun could hear the distant rumble of Russian heavy artillery, he received a teletype message from Kammler in Nordhausen. EW was ordered to abandon Peenemünde, move to

Nordhausen, and continue its operations around the underground factory there. This was part of a plan to relocate all key weapon projects to central Germany, beyond the immediate reach of the Allied armies.

On the same day, however, von Braun received a conflicting order from the commander of the Army Group charged with defending Pomerania, the state which included Peenemünde. The engineers at EW were ordered to join the *Volkssturm*, the People's Army, and to remain on Usedom Island to defend it against the advancing Russians.

The directly conflicting orders typified for von Braun the bizzare situation existing in a disintegrating Germany. Either could be followed, for both were binding in the overlapping command structures of a country where no one was certain any longer of who was in charge of what. More than one of his engineers had told von Braun that a large-scale exodus to the west could not be successfully managed and that the wisest course was to stay put, on the theory that the Russians, who had no long-range rockets, would undoubtedly give favored treatment to those German rocket specialists who survived the battle for Usedom Island.

Von Braun had already discussed the future of EW with a few of his closest associates. None of them wanted the rocket or themselves to fall into Russian hands. Von Braun lost no time in deciding that Kammler's order was the one to follow. It would move EW away from the Russians and into the path of the British and American armies.

The decision required moving some five thousand people, including families with young children, 250 miles south. During the day, the roads and railways lines that would have to be used were continually strafed by Allied planes. But the EW equipment was crated and transport and lists of those to go were assembled. A hundred trucks and two trains with instructions to move only at night, were sent southward in staggered shifts. Everything of scientific value that could be moved, including the all-important technical documents, was taken.

The first train, carrying over five hundred technicians and their families, left Peenemünde on February 17, 1945. Von Braun flew to Nordhausen to survey the new location of EW, flew back to Peenemünde, and accompanied one of the first truck convoys. He ran into a roadblock set up by Army troops at Eberswalde, a city on the railroad line between Peenemünde and Berlin, and was told by the major in charge that civilian traffic was forbidden in the area. It was an anxious moment for von Braun. If the major checked with the Army Group commander who had ordered the EW engineers to join the *Volkssturm* and remain at Peenemünde, the entire convoy could find itself rerouted back to Usedom Island.

For the first and last time, von Braun was glad that Himmler had succeeded in taking over the rocket program. Von Braun had taken the precaution of having letterheads and passes printed that stressed EW's association with the SS leader. And all of the trucks, trains, and equipment had been plastered with stickers bearing the fictitious and meaningless designation *VZBV*.

When the major refused to let the convoy through the roadblock, von Braun, who recalls that they "faced each other like bulldogs," improvised. He informed the major that *VZBV* stood for *Vorhaben zur besonderen Verwendung* (Project for Special Dispositions), a top-secret undertaking ordered to move to central Germany by Himmler himself. Von Braun sounded convincing, and in the Third Reich of February 1945 few people were prepared to dispute the wishes of Himmler and the SS. The major finally permitted the civilian convoy to continue its journey.

By the middle of March, when the Red Army had taken Swinemünde, only twenty-five miles from Peenemünde, the exodus to central Germany had been completed. The rocket specialists and their families were resettled in villages scattered around Nordhausen, with the largest number in the cotton-mill town of Bleicherode. General Dornberger and his staff moved from the Ministry of Munitions in Berlin to the nearby hot-springs resort of Bad Sachsa.

A migration of this size could not be hidden from Allied intelligence agents. Soviet Intelligence, which had every reason to believe that it would capture all the German rocket specialists, quickly learned that they had left Peenemünde and where they had gone. And when infantry of the Second White Russian Army under Major Anatole Vavilov eventually stormed Peenemünde on May 5, 1945, no one of technical importance was found among the skeleton staff which had been left behind. The Russian technical intelligence teams which followed the combat troops were further frustrated to discover that there were no essential documents and blueprints at Peenemünde and that the research buildings and test stands—which had already been battered in the British and American air raids—had been partially blown up by the *Volkssturm* even as Vavilov's infantry approached. The great rocket center was, according to Vavilov, "seventy-five per cent wreckage." [3]

The Russians, however, were able to assemble from the ruins of Peenemünde an accurate picture of what had gone on there and an accurate list of its departed leading figures. Although Soviet Intelligence had failed to capture either Dornberger, von Braun, Steinhoff, and other key specialists or large quantities of intact V-2's and the V-2 technician documents, it did not abandon its determination to do so eventually. British Intelligence was after the same things, but in March 1945 it appeared that the prize would now fall to the Americans, whose troops were heading toward Thuringia and seemed certain to capture Nordhausen and Bleicherode. Despite this accident of geography which shifted the advantage to the United States, the British, like the Russians, did not abandon their efforts.

In Nordhausen-Bleicherode, von Braun, believing that the total collapse of the Third Reich was only a matter of time and that continued work on V-2 and other weapons with the object of preventing that collapse was a farcical undertaking, drove ahead with research and development. While there was still time, the art of rocketry itself could be advanced. Test stands were built at Lehesten and Leutenberg. Experimentation was continued in the underground *Mittelwerke* factory, in abandoned power plants, garages, empty castles— any place that would offer shelter.

When von Braun discovered that a new valve laboratory was needed, he searched the countryside and near Jena found the huge old hilltop fortress of Leuchtenberg. It could be transformed into what he needed. He decided to drive to Berlin to pry funds loose for the necessary construction work.

He left Bleicherode at two o'clock in the morning of March 16, hoping to reach the Ministry of Munitions before daybreak and the appearance of the Allied planes, which strafed anything that moved on the roads. His young civilian driver drove their compact car, a Hannomag Storm, through Naumburg, got on the autobahn near Weissenfels, and sped toward Berlin with dimmed lights. Von Braun, who'd had little sleep in the past two months, dozed off.

He was awakened by a queer sensation which, as he remembers it, made him think briefly that he was back in the glider he had enjoyed flying before the war. The Storm, in fact, was soaring through the air. The tired driver had dozed off, too, on the monotonous gray stretch of autobahn. He had lost control of the car, and it swerved over a railroad embankment, plunged downward, and smashed into a siding. Von Braun remembers shouldering open a door, pulling the unconscious driver away from the wreck just before its motor caught fire, and becoming aware of searing pain in his left arm, which was dangling below his knee. Then he blacked out.

The autobahn was deserted at that bleak early hour, and it is quite possible that von Braun and his driver, both unconscious, could have bled to death under the railroad embankment but for the fortuitous appearance of another car. Before leaving for Berlin, von Braun had instructed Hannes Luehrsen, EW's chief architect, and Bernhard Tessmann, chief designer of its test facilities, to meet him at the Ministry of Munitions to assist him in arguing the case for transforming the Leuchtenberg fortress into a valve laboratory. Tessmann and Luehrsen happened to be following von Braun's car and saw it shoot over the railroad embankment. They pulled up, scrambled down to the siding, administered what first aid they could, and then drove off to find an ambulance. It was four hours before they were able to return with one.

Von Braun's driver was found to have suffered a fractured skull in the accident, but he survived. Von Braun's left arm, which had been broken in two places, and his shattered left shoulder were pieced together in a hospital. Cuts he had suffered on his face were patched and a gash over his lips sewn. He still carries a slight scar over his upper lip, and to this day his left arm is slightly crooked.

Von Braun argued his way out of the hospital on March 21, eager to get research and development moving again. With his chest and left arm encased in a huge plaster cast, he took up residence in the large modern house of one of the cotton-mill tycoons of Bleicherode. A party was held there on March 23, von Braun's thirty-third birthday, attended by Dornberger and his young wife and many of von Braun's associates who had worked with him since their first primitive rocket experiments in the early thirties. They tried to be gay and talk of other things besides the war. It was a false gaiety. All of them knew that the Russians were overrunning eastern Germany and advancing toward the Elbe River, and that the British and Americans would soon cross the Rhine, drive through central Germany, and meet the Russians on the Elbe. All of them knew that no rocket development could be continued in Germany for more than two months, probably less. The end was in sight, and the chances that any of them would be able to continue rocket work in the bleak future appeared so slim as to be nonexistent.

None of them, of course, could know that their future was a subject of interest to certain technical experts in all three of the major Allied countries, and that their names figured prominently on a top-secret list of German scientific targets compiled by British and American Intelligence. In the description of Major Robert Staver, one of the Americans who compiled the list, the targets were those "whose exploitation is expected to yield information of military importance, either of such great value to the Allies for operational purposes or constituting such a dangerous potential threat in the future as to justify urgent action on the part of the Allies in seizing them both before and immediately after the armistice. . . ."[4]

The target list bore the code name "Black List."

# PART TWO
# OVERCAST

# Black list

Six weeks before von Braun's birthday party in central Germany, Robert Staver, a twenty-eight-year-old major in U. S. Army Ordnance, had arrived in London. As Staver was reporting to his commanding officer, Major Calvin Corey, in an office building at 27 Grosvenor Square, both men were shaken and thrown to the floor by a terrific blast.

Staver got up, looked out the window, and, as he remembers it, saw "a big round cloud of smoke where a V-2 had exploded overhead." As hot metal rained down on Grosvenor Square, Staver calculated that the missile had been heading "very directly at us" but had exploded prematurely in the air.

This was not Staver's last encounter with V-2 at close hand. He was billeted in a hotel near the Marble Arch and one evening was thrown out of bed by another terrific blast which, he recalls, "made the drapes of my window stand straight out from the wall." A V-2 had landed in Hyde Park just beyond the Marble Arch, killing sixty-two soapbox orators and their listeners. And when Staver was driving on Ordnance business to the Royal Aircraft Establishment at Farnborough with Ed Hull, an American civil engineer, a V-2 scored a chance direct hit on a roadside Packard warehouse half a mile ahead of them. Staver and Hull stopped to examine the crater and the damage. Hundreds of new Rolls-

Merlin aircraft engines in the warehouse had been demolished and fifteen workers killed.

Staver had good reason to take careful note of the effect of the V-2's. He had been sent to Europe by Army Ordnance to investigate those Black List targets having to do with German rockets and guided missiles. He was part of what would become a vast hunt for the secrets of German science launched by all of the Allies as the war drew to a close.

The hunt was spurred by a fact that was obvious to the technical experts: the Germans had failed in the key field of atomic research, but they had succeeded in developing many new devices that were much more advanced than anything the Allies possessed. The electric-powered U-Boat, the jet plane, and the long-range rocket were only the most spectacular in a long list of prizes that awaited the enterprising victor.

The German failure to develop an atom bomb was discovered by the Allies through the efforts of Alsos,[1] the first large-scale scientific intelligence mission in history, whose objectives took precedence over every other German target, including V-2. When the very real fears that the Germans might have developed an atom bomb proved to be groundless, scientific intelligence turned to other targets.

V-2 was one, but only one, of the prizes sought by technical intelligence units organized by the various branches of the American armed forces. A misconception has persisted since World War II that this massive search was a coordinated effort called *Operation Paperclip*. In the spring of 1945, when it began, the venture had no name. Units representing the Army, Army Air Forces, and Navy simply went into Germany to find out what they could, frequently competing with each other as well as with their British and Russian counterparts. It was not until July 1945 that this free-wheeling, overall operation was formalized under the secret code name *Overcast*.*

* It was not until March 13, 1946, that, owing to a security leak, the

Of all the American agencies that would become involved in *Overcast,* one agency, and one man, had from the beginning displayed the greatest interest in V-2. In September 1943, Colonel Gervais William Trichel, of Trichel, Louisiana, a 1918 graduate of West Point with a master of science degree from M I T and a doctorate in electrical engineering from the University of California, had been appointed to a newly created post in Army Ordnance: Chief, Rocket Branch.

After the first V-2's had been put into action in September 1944, Colonel Trichel received reports on their performance from Europe which made him realize that the United States, like England and Russia, was at least twenty years behind the Germans in rocket development. As Germany's defeat became a certainty, Trichel saw an opportunity. If intact V-2's, their technical data and blueprints, and interrogations of the men who had developed the world's first long-range rocket could be placed at his disposal, his small Army Ordnance Rocket Branch would be able to pick up where the Germans had left off. Millions of dollars and twenty years of research and development time would be saved.

Colonel Trichel acted to capitalize on the opportunity in two ways. In late 1944 he had negotiated a contract with the General Electric Company for Project Hermes, in which General Electric was to research and develop long-range guided missiles for Army Ordnance. Ordnance established a test firing range at the White Sands Proving Ground in the New Mexico desert, and Trichel felt that it would be a great help to the Project Hermes engineers to study and fire some live V-2's there. In March 1945 he sent a request to Colonel Holger Toftoy, Chief of Ordnance Technical Intelligence, in Paris, who was responsible for capturing new German

---

code name of this secret project was changed from *Overcast* to *Paperclip.* An account of *Overcast/Paperclip,* an undertaking unique in American history and one which involved German specialists in many fields other than rocketry, will be found in the Appendix.

operational weapons and shipping them back to the States for study. Trichel urged Toftoy to find one hundred V-2's in good operational condition and to ship them to New Mexico.

To direct the location and interrogation of the German guided-missile specialists and the securing of the V-2 documents for the United States, Colonel Trichel had already sent Major Robert Staver to London in February. Staver had graduated from Stanford in 1940 with a mechanical engineering degree and had three years of experience in Army Ordnance rocket development. He reported for duty as Chief, Rocket Section, Combined Intelligence Objectives Sub-Committee,* Liaison Branch of the Technical Division, Office of the Chief Ordnance Officer. This jawbreaking designation, while formidable enough, was not as formidable as the job that confronted Staver.

First he had to compile lists of hundreds of installations from the Baltic to the Swiss border where the Germans were working on jet propulsion and guided missiles. Then he had to compile lists of the thousands of technicians who were working at those installations. Finally, he had to grade his lists as to importance. He put the key targets on a "Black List" and targets of lesser importance on a "Gray List."

After two months of working twelve hours a day, seven days a week, in his tiny office at 27 Grosvenor Square, Staver compiled accurate, workable lists. He could not have done

* The Combined Intelligence Objectives Sub-Committee, known as CIOS, had been created by the British-American Combined Chiefs of Staff in the summer of 1944 to plan and administer an orderly exploitation of German scientific targets. Officers from the technical branches of the British and American armed forces were assigned to CIOS and were assisted by civilian scientists. They were to pool information about German weapons that might have future research and development applications. Ordnance, as the U. S. Army service concerned with weapons, supplied the greatest American representation on CIOS. In addition to Staver's Rocket Section, there were Ordnance groups assigned to ammunition, explosives, artillery, miscellaneous chemicals, and metallurgy.

so, however, without British cooperation. In view of the struggle which would later take place among the Americans, Russians, and British for the V-2 spoils of war, a competition in which the British would finish last, Staver would come to appreciate the irony of this situation.

According to Staver, his counterparts among the British rocket experts gave him 90 percent of his target intelligence. They gave him all the information they had gathered on Peenemünde during the secret weapon investigation. They also gave him a remarkably detailed Target Information Sheet, complete with aerial photographs, which pinpointed Nordhausen as the major source of V-weapon manufacture and as the new location of the German rocket specialists.

The British gave Staver not only complete descriptions of Peenemünde and Nordhausen but also the names of the key personnel of those installations. Until the borders of Germany itself had been crossed, the identity of the men responsible for the V-weapons had largely remained a secret. But from many sources this secret was now gradually being unlocked. Hundreds of thousands of prisoners of war, some of whom had been assigned to weapon operations, were available for interrogation. Revealing documents were found in the abandoned launching sites in northern France and Holland and in captured factories which had supplied fuels and components to Nordhausen and Peenemünde. The most informative find, however, was a single document—the Osenberg List.

Osenberg, a journeyman professor of mechanical engineering at the University of Hannover, a good Nazi and a member of the SS, had been placed in charge of the Planning Office of the Reich's Research Council by Goering. With Teutonic thoroughness, Osenberg compiled a complete card index of all wartime scientific projects and of the scientists and engineers assigned to them. Osenberg not only compiled a list of fifteen thousand people but also had the Gestapo check on their loyalty to the regime and note whatever personal idiosyncrasies each might have: alcoholism, wife beating, the collection of pornography, homosexuality, keeping a mistress, having given prewar lectures in the United States or in England. Osenberg found his list very helpful in controlling the German scientific community, of which he was the official major-domo.

On March 7, 1945, the U. S. 3rd Armored Division occupied Cologne. Bonn, thirteen miles to the north, would remain under German control for another two days and at the university there the destruction of papers relating to scientific research on weapons was ordered. Secret papers were burned or torn up and flushed down toilets as the American tanks approached. In a toilet bowl that hadn't flushed properly, a Polish laboratory technician found shredded pieces of paper, which he later gave to a British Intelligence agent. Dried out and pieced together, the papers turned out to be the Osenberg List, which included, of course, the names and responsibilities of German rocket personnel.

British Intelligence searched for similar leads in captured Gestapo files. Practically all of these, however, were destroyed as the Germans retreated, but a few survived where departure was especially hasty.

From leads such as these, Major Staver was able to compile his Black List. Heading it, he placed Combined Intelligence Objectives Sub-Committee item 4/113 (b), Nordhausen, and the name Professor Dr. Wernher Freiherr von Braun.

Compiling the Black List was one thing, Staver knew, but tracking down the targets on it was another, although a system had been set up for doing so. Following the combat troops, a special "T-Force" of soldiers with varied technical and language skills would secure and guard targets judged to be of scientific intelligence value. They would be followed by teams of CAFT (Combined Advance Field Team) technical assessors, who would evaluate the secured targets. If the latter proved to be of more than average importance, the CAFT assessors would recommend that American civilian scientists be called in to conduct an investigation in depth.

In March 1945, Colonel Trichel had sent to London a team of General Electric Scientists from Project Hermes.[2] It was Major Staver's assignment to direct this team to the V-2 target, which Staver would pinpoint through the Black List, the T-Forces, and the CAFT assessors. As for finding and securing the V-2 technical documents for the United States, Staver, in March 1945, could have no certain idea of how to accomplish this mission. Those documents alone, he often told himself, would give the Army Ordnance Rocket Branch the twenty-year advantage which its chief, Colonel Trichel, was hoping for, even without the General Electric team's interrogations of the men who had produced the documents. But the Germans might destroy the documents or hide them as the enemy approached.

In any case, nothing could be done about finding the documents or the V-2 personnel until the Nordhausen-Bleicherode area had been taken. G-2, U. S. Military Intelligence, had an ironclad rule forbidding technical investigators from entering combat zones until they had been cleared of all enemy resistance. To the American military leaders, scientific intelligence investigations were a footnote to the key objective of crushing the German armed forces. They wanted nothing to impede front-line operations and did not want the responsibility of the safety of eminent American civilian scientists.

As eager as he was to get moving, this ban did not disturb Major Staver. He realized that the British and the Russians must be after the same targets that he was, but he knew they would fall to the army that reached Nordhausen and Bleicherode first. Staver was confident that the British, and especially the Russians, were not going to fall heir to the world's first long-range guided missile and use it to gain a head start in a postwar rocket development program. He became doubly certain when on April 1, in London, he received word that units of the U. S. First Army had taken the German city of Paderborn and were preparing a drive eastward to the Elbe River. Only ninety miles from Paderborn and in the direct line of advance of "Lucky Spearhead," the 3rd Armored Division, were Nordhausen and Bleicherode.

# Burial

On the afternoon of April 1, Easter Sunday, von Braun, in Bleicherode, heard that American tanks had been seen in Mühlhausen, twelve miles south. This was a false rumor, although von Braun could not know that fact. He did realize, however, that the end was in sight. Hitler realized it too. Now a trembling wreck, poisoned by Dr. Morell's drugs, screaming at his generals, the Führer decided that the German people had failed to meet the challenge of history and were destined for destruction. On March 19 he had issued an order to both the SS and the Army that everything of possible value to the approaching enemy must be destroyed. This included all research installations and their technical documents.

Albert Speer, Minister of Armaments and War Production, tried to reason with Hitler, but the Führer shouted at him: "If the war is lost, the nation will also perish . . . it will be better to destroy these things ourselves because this nation will have proved to be the weaker one and the future will belong solely to the stronger eastern nation. Besides, those who will remain after the battle are only the inferior ones, for the good ones have been killed." [1]

Von Braun had learned of Hitler's scorched-earth directive

and felt that Speer might not be able to prevent the SS from executing it. The SS could not be stopped from razing the installations at Nordhausen-Bleicherode, von Braun knew, but he also knew that the installations were not as important as the thoughts that had gone on in the brains of the Peenemünde team, thoughts that had been set down in tons of documents and blueprints. It had taken sixty-five-thousand drawings alone to produce the first successful A-4. Nazi Germany, the SS, and the Führer were not dead yet, but they clearly belonged to the past. The rocket and all the paper work that had gone into it belonged to the future. Von Braun decided to disobey Hitler's scorched-earth directive and preserve the V-2 documents, which represented a treasure of technical information unique in the world. Dornberger strongly supported this decision, though both men knew that it might involve them in serious trouble with the SS.

The report of American tanks in Mühlhausen on April 1 caused von Braun to act. He called in two men he felt he could trust, Dieter Huzel and Bernhard Tessman. Huzel was an electrical engineer who had been drafted as a private by the German Army in 1942 and assigned to driving trucks on the Russian front. Later he had been assigned to Peenemünde, and while he had never been one of its leading figures, he had served as von Braun's personal aide. Tessmann, an old associate of von Braun's, had been the chief designer of the test facilities at Peenemünde. It was Tessman, along with Hannes Luehrsen, who had found von Braun lying bleeding and unconscious under the railroad embankment after the automobile accident of March 16, an intervention that had saved von Braun's life.

Von Braun now gave Tessmann and Huzel an unusual and difficult assignment. They were to collect all of the key V-2 technical documents from Nordhausen, Bleicherode, and surrounding areas, load them into trucks, and then hide them. Huzel recalls von Braun telling him, "Probably the best possibility is an old mine or a cave—something of that sort. Other than that, I have no specific thoughts. There is just no time to lose."

On that Easter Sunday afternoon, Hans Kammler, too, heard that the Americans were nearing Nordhausen and Bleicherode. Besides being Special Commissioner for the V-weapon program, General Kammler was now also Special Commissioner for "Breaking the Air Terror" and General Commissioner for Turbojet Fighters. The V-weapons were no longer being fired, so Kammler concentrated on his other posts, only to find armadas of Allied bombers and fighters sweeping through German skies despite his most frantic efforts.

"He was on the move day and night," General Dornberger observed. "Conferences were called for one o'clock in the morning somewhere in the Harz Mountains, or we would meet at midnight somewhere on the autobahn and then, after a brief exchange of views, drive back to work again. We were prey to terrific nervous tension. Irritable and overworked as we were, we didn't mince words. Kammler, if he got impatient and wanted to drive on, would wake the slumbering officers of his suite with a burst from his tommy-gun. 'No need for them to sleep! I can't either!' "

Dornberger realized that the Special Commissioner's state of mind was changing from the irritable to the dangerously desperate when he overheard a conversation between Kammler and his chief of staff, SS Major Starck. According to Dornberger, Kammler ordered his chief of staff to follow him constantly at ten paces carrying a machine pistol; if the situation became hopeless, Starck—without waiting to ask questions—was ordered to fire a burst into the back of Kammler's head.

SS General Kammler had reason to be distraught by the news of the Americans' approach. He had organized and directed the use of concentration-camp labor in V-weapon production. There were two concentration camps in the Nordhausen area, one in Nordhausen itself and another two and a half miles away at Dora, on the southern side of the *Mittelwerke*. At the height of V-weapon production, twenty-two thousand prisoners from these two camps had toiled in the tunnels of the underground factory. While they were of use, the prisoners had been relatively well treated, but conditions had deteriorated in the last two months, especially at Nordhausen, which housed thousands of political prisoners and other "undesirables" who had not been assigned to V-weapon production. When the Americans entered the Dora and Nordhausen camps, they would probably hang the man responsible for what they found there. That man, Kammler knew, was himself. Desperate, he ordered his SS guards to move the prisoners out of the two camps and to kill and bury those who could not be moved.

As desperate as he was, however, Kammler had not lost hope or any of the quick-witted shrewdness or talent for improvisation that had gained him the post of Special Commissioner over more technically qualified men. He had no intention of being captured and hanged by the Americans, because he did not intend to be in Nordhausen when they arrived. He had, in fact, thought of a bizarre plan to save his own neck. On April 1 he decided to put it into effect.

Out of the approximately five thousand rocket specialists and their families who were living around Nordhausen in the province of Thuringia in central Germany, the area being approached by American troops, Kammler would select five hundred of the leading figures. These men, without their families, would be sent four hundred miles south to the Bavarian Alps under a heavy guard of SD* men, the security service of the SS. Once in the remote fastnesses of the Alps, the five hundred specialists could be used as hostages. Kammler could bargain with the Americans or one of

* *Sicherheits-Dienst.*

the other Allies for his own life in exchange for the leading German rocket specialists. If no bargain could be made, the rocket men could simply be shot to deny their talents to the enemies of the Third Reich.

Kammler called in von Braun and told him that he and five hundred of his key men would be moved on Kammler's special train to the Alpine Redoubt, to which, according to Kammler, the Führer and all the SS divisions in the Third Reich were also moving to regroup for the final victory. A former Army camp at Oberammergau would be made available to the rocket men to continue their research. They would be protected by a special SD detachment. The move was to start immediately; there was no time to take any families or equipment.

Von Braun knew that Kammler was too shrewd to believe in the Alpine Redoubt and suspected that the Special Commissioner wanted the leading rocket men concentrated in a small area under SS control for some sinister purpose of his own. Given Kammler's present state of mind, however, there was nothing to be gained by contesting his directive. Kammler was still in full control of his shrinking empire. It was within his power to have his SS men execute anyone who refused to obey his orders. Von Braun decided that the lesser of two evils was relocation to the Alps. Even without equipment, some research could be continued there. And von Braun, like Kammler, had a plan for the future. It was a plan that envisioned large-scale rocket development after the Third Reich was dead and the war was over. Von Braun felt that in the Bavarian mountains a chance existed to escape the "protection" of the SD and put his plan into effect. General Dornberger, though he was now assigned to other weapon projects in addition to being connected with the rocket program, had also chosen to move to a village in the Alps close to where his former Peenemünde men would be billeted. Dornberger suspected that Kammler and the SD might cause trouble. Therefore, he brought with him a detachment of Army soldiers which had been assigned to him.

By dusk of April 2 the selection of scientists and engineers had been made. They gathered their personal belongings, said good-bye to their families, and entered the compartments of the Vergeltungs-Express. The "Vengeance Express," as Kammler's private train was sardonically referred to, consisted of a sleek, modern engine, twelve sleeping cars, and a dining car. The latter was well stocked with food and the fine wines to which Kammler was partial. As Special Commissioner, he had used the train to move himself and members of his staff to all points in Europe where there was V-weapon activity, from Peenemünde to Nordhausen, and from Holland to Berlin and southern Poland. Until the firing range at Blizna had been abandoned in the face of the Red Army advance, the V-Express had often been stationed there. It served Kammler, his officers, and many prominent technicians as living quarters which were much more comfortable than the crude wooden barracks surrounding the launching sites.

The V-Express, jammed with five hundred civilian rocket specialists and almost one hundred armed SD guards, pulled out of Nordhausen to begin its four-hundred-mile journey southward to the Alps. Von Braun, however, was not aboard. Because of the huge cast encasing his torso and left arm, he received permission to follow in a passenger car. As he was driven toward Munich, he wondered what the future held, and especially if Huzel and Tessmann had been successful in hiding the key V-2 documents.

On the rainy morning of Tuesday, April 3, a passenger car driven by a uniformed German soldier threaded its way through the winding side roads of the Harz Mountains. Dieter Huzel sat next to the driver. Behind them came Bernhard Tessmann and seven soldiers in the cabs of three 3-ton

Opel trucks, two of them with trailers attached. These vehicles were jammed with all the V-2 documents which would, in Huzel's phrase, "be essential should we resume our work."

All nonessential material had been burned on Monday and Tuesday. Huzel and Tessmann had also spent these days in the Nordhausen-Bleicherode area supervising the collection, crating, and loading of the key documents. Fourteen tons of paper had been placed in wooden boxes. And on the sides of these crates, numbers had been written and stenciled for future identification. As Huzel led the convoy out of Nordhausen and into the mountains, he had no clear idea where the documents should be hidden. Von Braun, before his own departure for the Alps, had given Huzel a letter of safe conduct. It stated that his mission was top secret and that he should be given every assistance. But von Braun had also said, accurately, "You're on your own."

Huzel decided to seek assistance at the headquarters of the government mining agency in Clausthal, thirty miles away. There he would inquire about the availability of a large cave in a mountainside or of an abandoned mine. The Harz Mountains were an area of wild and melancholy beauty, of ravines, crags, dark green woods, and snug little towns with ancient half-timbered houses. Many of these towns were spas and climatic health resorts; others for centuries had been engaged in the mining of lead, copper, silver, and iron.

The three heavily laden trucks moved slowly, pausing several times to take cover under trees as fighter planes flashed overhead. By noon they reached a hamlet in a narrow valley five miles from Clausthal. The valley appeared to offer good protection from attacks by strafing fighters. The trucks were parked there, and Huzel drove on alone to the mining agency headquarters. There he was told that nothing in the area would suit his requirements. For a major unloading and storing operation, a mine with a horizontal entrance served by rails was essential. All the nearby mines had vertical shafts and elevators. They were also active, which meant that the storage of boxes in them could not be hidden from the notice of hundreds of miners. A mining official suggested that Huzel might have better luck at the suboffice in Goslar, fifteen miles away.

Growing desperate and wondering if anything had happened to the trucks parked in the valley, Huzel raced to Goslar. Again he was told by an official that his requirements could not be filled. All the mines in the area were already jammed with government files brought down from Berlin. Angered and frustrated, Huzel remembers that he shouted at the official: "Here I stand, with the most important documents in Germany! And I can't even find a place to put them." As he stormed toward the door, the official called him back; he had just remembered an old abandoned mine in the village of Dörnten, ten miles away. It was not in the mountains but was three miles from the northern edge of the Harz. It might, however, be suitable.

Huzel and the official sped to Dörnten. Just outside of the tiny, isolated village they drew up before the elevator tower of a vertical shaft. But beyond it they saw another, horizontal mine cut into a low, sloping hill. Both mines had been abandoned because they yielded iron ore of such poor quality that it was not economical to continue working them. The only people in the vicinity were an elderly couple; the man, whose name was Nebelung, served as caretaker.

Nebelung immediately offered his cooperation when Huzel told him that he wanted to store important classified military information in the tunnel of the horizontal mine. Huzel did not tell either Nebelung or the mining official that the "information" represented everything that was known about the world's first long-range guided missile. The caretaker supplied his visitors with work clothes, miners' hats, battery lamps, and then led them to the mouth of a tunnel which led into the hillside.

Huzel saw a loading ramp, switches, and rails going into darkness. In the eerie light cast by the battery lamps, he followed Nebelung down the track. On both sides of it small galleries branched off. After they had walked for about a thousand feet, Nebelung stopped, flashed his lamp into one of the galleries, and said that at its end was a dry, empty room. It had once been used to store mine explosives. The men walked down the gallery for a hundred yards. Here they came to a heavy iron door, which they opened, to find a room about twelve feet high and twenty-five feet square. Huzel remembers thinking that it was "perfect" for his purpose. But the problem remained of how he and Tessmann and the seven soldiers could move fourteen tons of boxes a thousand yards down the railroad track to the gallery entrance before American combat troops, which were thirty miles away, overran the area in which the mine was located.

Nebelung offered a possible solution. There were flatcars and a small electric-battery-operated locomotive on the premises. The locomotive had not been used for years, but the caretaker could recharge its batteries and might be able to have it in working order by the next day. Huzel had no alternative but to accept this offer. He raced back to the narrow valley where the three trucks had been parked and saw with great relief that they were still there and unharmed. He outlined a plan of action to Bernhard Tessmann. The trucks would be driven to an old quarry in another sheltered valley five miles from the Dörnten mine. From this base of operations the trucks would be driven to the mine one by one just after nightfall.

Huzel, however, did not want the seven soldiers to know the exact location of the mine. They might be captured later by American troops and reveal the secret of the hiding place. Huzel decided that he would drive the first truck to the mine, with Tessmann sitting next to him. The soldiers would be locked in the back of the truck until it reached the tunnel entrance. After it had been unloaded, Huzel would drive it back to the quarry. There he would pick up the second truck and repeat the procedure with the third.

Through the night of April 4 and well into the following morning, boxes were unloaded from the three trucks, reloaded onto the flatcars, and hauled by the small locomotive to the gallery entrance. Here the nine sweating, struggling Germans had to unload the boxes once again and carry them a hundred yards into the former powder magazine. "Until almost eleven in the morning," Huzel recalls, "we worked at hard physical labor. The boxes were heavy. The gallery leading to the storage room was narrow and uphill."

When the last box had been stored, almost filling the small room, Huzel remembers thinking: "Mission accomplished, and all of a sudden I felt dead tired. I looked around, and I saw my weariness reflected in the faces of the others, leaning against the wall, squatting on the floor, or standing with hands on hips, covered with sweat and utterly disarrayed."

The exhausted men left the tunnel for a shower and then lunch at the deserted mine cafeteria. Huzel obtained from Nebelung his agreement to dynamite the gallery leading to the old powder magazine. Then Huzel, Tessman, and the soldiers drove away from the mine and spent the night of Thursday, April 5, in a nearby village. The two engineers drove back to the mine the next morning. Huzel found that the dynamiting job "was not really satisfactory; rocks blasted from the roof had formed a heap below, but it was still an easy matter to clamber over this into the storage room." He urged Nebelung to complete the job.

After he and Tessmann had left, Nebelung set off another charge of dynamite. It sealed off the small room completely. The V-2 documents were now a buried treasure. To those who had no interest in building big long-range rockets, the cache hidden in the Dörnten mine could consist only of four-teen tons of "technical" papers. To those who were inter-ested and could find the hiding place, the papers represented thirteen years of unique research work and the complete plans for an object which had cost the Third Reich between four and five hundred million dollars to produce.

On Saturday, April 7, Huzel and Tessmann, satisfied that Nebelung had completed the blasting job, left the Dörnten area just as troops of the U. S. Ninth Army arrived. The two Germans returned to Bleicherode. On that day they were the only men who knew the exact location of the V-2 docu-ments. The soldiers who had helped them had, of course, been locked inside the trucks on the approach to and the departure from the abandoned mine. Nebelung and the mining official from the Goslar suboffice knew where the mine was and that documents had been hidden there, but they had not been told that they were the V-2 documents.

Upon reaching Nordhausen-Bleicherode, Huzel and Tess-mann did not remain there very long. The false rumor of April 1 had become fact. American troops were now closing in on the area. On April 9, Tessmann headed for the Alps, four hundred miles away, and a rendezvous with von Braun and the five hundred technicians who were working there under SD surveillance. Huzel made a quick trip north to Berlin to collect his fiancée and then also drove to the Alps.

Work stopped at the *Mittelwerke* on April 10. The forty-five hundred remaining rocket technicians (who had not been sent to the Alps by Kammler) drifted away to their homes in scores of villages surrounding Nordhausen. A re-port was confirmd that American tanks had reached Esp-chenrode, six miles from the underground factory.

# 10

## Lucky Spearhead

To the advance tank units, or Task Forces, of the U.S. 3rd Armored Division which approached Espchenrode on April 10, Nordhausen was just another German city to be taken on the drive to the Elbe River and a link-up with the Red Army.

The 3rd Armored had started in Normandy, fought through France and the Bulge, and begun a swift drive over the Remagen bridgehead on March 25, 1945. On the dark evening of March 30, just as the Ruhr was about to be encircled, "Lucky Spearhead's" commanding general, Maurice Rose, had been killed in a confused, vicious action with marauding Tiger and Panther tanks.

Angered, the 3rd Armored had knifed into the heart of Germany and crossed the Weser River, forty-five miles from Nordhausen, on April 9. But none of the tankers of the 3rd Armored, or the infantrymen of the 104th "Timberwolf" Division who supported them, had ever heard of Wernher von Braun, Walter Dornberger, or the underground *Mittelwerke*. They had heard of V-2, but by April 1945 it was a memory, something that had caused sudden explosions in the leave areas of London and Brussels the preceding fall and winter. Because of its limited accuracy at long range,

V-2 had never been used against combat troops, who were much more concerned with King Tiger tanks, plastic mines, and the deadly 88 artillery pieces.

There were no technical intelligence specialists or American civilian scientists with the 3rd Armored Task Forces as they approached Espchenrode and Nordhausen. Wherever "Lucky Spearhead" was engaged, action was extremely hot and fast-moving. Scientific spies would only have gotten in the way and hampered the principal job of the men in the rolling Sherman tanks: to destroy the German armed forces in the field and end the war. The British and Russians, too, held back their technical investigators from unsecured combat areas. Any other policy would have been fruitless; for the investigation of targets of the complexity and magnitude of V-2, careful advance planning, time, and quiet were essential.

When Task Force Welborn of the 3rd Armored struck toward Nordhausen on April 10, it ran into unexpectedly stiff resistance at the hamlet of Espchenrode. Six companies of first-rate troops led by fanatical SS officers (sent to stem the American advance by Hans Kammler) had to be wiped out by tanks, strafing P-47 Thunderbolts, and infantry in savage house-to-house fighting that lasted four hours.

Early the next morning, Brigadier General Truman Boudinot's Combat Command "B" rolled into Nordhausen itself with little opposition. Its two task forces, the northern assault element under Colonel John C. Welborn and the southern element under Lieutenant Colonel William B. Lovelady, converged on the center of the smoking, ruined city at about the same time. "Lucky Spearhead" was ordered to pause in Nordhausen until relieved by infantry of the Timberwolf Division and then resume its drive eastward. For the combat tankers, Nordhausen was an episode that was now closed.

Colonel Welborn, however, had been alerted by Military

Intelligence to "expect something a little unusual in the Nordhausen area." So had General Boudinot and Lieutenant Colonel Lovelady. They had all noted this rather vague report and, as combat men who knew from hard experience how wrong rear-echelon intelligence could often be, had taken it with the usual grain of salt.

They weren't in the smoldering wreckage of Nordhausen twenty minutes, however, when they realized that this time the Military Intelligence forecast had been understated. What Combat Command "B" found was not just "a little unusual," but enough to sicken Truman Boudinot, a man whom the GI's of the 3rd Armored considered tougher than George Patton.

Boudinot was taken into the Nordhausen concentration camp and saw hundreds of corpses lying out in the open and hundreds more in the barracks. They "lay in contorted heaps, half stripped, mouths gaping in the dirt and straw; or they were piled naked, like cordwood, in the corners or under the staircases."

The stench of decomposing bodies clogged the air. Some living beings, ragged "skin-covered skeletons," weaved and tottered forward to greet Boudinot and his aides. There were a thousand of these "half-men" in Camp Nordhausen and five thousand corpses "in various stages of decay."

General Boudinot had never seen anything like this, and he would never forget it. He wanted to get his Combat Command moving out of this place, but there was something even more "unusual" in store before the day was over. Two and a half miles northwest of Nordhausen, in the village of Niedersachswerfen on the southern slopes of the Harz, Welborn and Lovelady encountered wraiths in dirty striped pajamas, babbling and waving their arms at them. Through interpreters, the two colonels heard that the skeletal figures wanted the Americans to know about "something fantastic —underneath the mountain . . . important . . ."

Berlin, August 1930: Hermann Oberth (dark coat, center), father of German rocket development, presents his Kegelduese, a small liquid-fuel rocket motor, for certification at the Chemisch-Technische Reichsanstalt, an organization comparable to the U. S. Bureau of Standards. Second from right is Oberth's assistant, eighteen-year-old Wernher von Braun. Early experiments such as these led to the A-4 (V-2), shown upper right, the world's first long-range rocket. It was put into action against the Allies in September 1944.

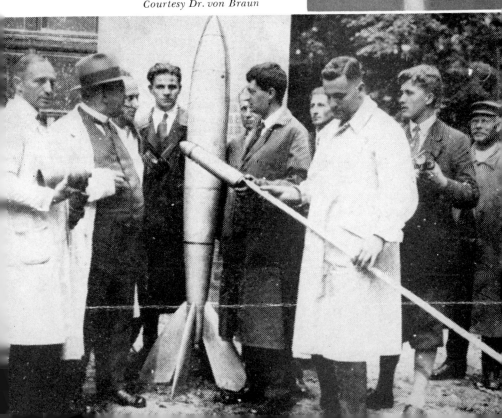

*Courtesy Dr. Dornberger*

Above: in leather coat and silk scarf, Heinrich Himmler makes his first inspection tour of Peenemünde in April 1943. On his left is Major General Dornberger. Below: test firing of an A-4 (V-2) at Peenemünde in May 1943. At extreme left, General Dornberger. Next to him, Field Marshal Walther von Brauchitsch, Commander in Chief of the German Army. The lone civilian is Dr. Wernher von Braun, technical director of Peenemünde's Army Experimental Station.

*Courtesy Dr. Dornberg*

Intelligence reports persuaded the British that the Germans were conducting extensive "secret weapon" experiments. The investigation of Peenemünde was largely carried out by aerial reconnaissance. This photograph of Test Stand VII, taken on June 23, 1943, was the first to reveal rockets. Two A-4's (V-2's) at least thirty-eight feet long are indicated lying horizontally at **A**. Buildings where rockets were stored are indicated at **B**.

The aerial photo (above) taken on the coast of northern France, November 9, 1943, was the first to reveal the puzzling construction of concrete buildings shaped like skis. These were meant to store V-1 components, whose actual firing points were nearby. Below is a V-1 buzz bomb captured intact after D-Day by U. S. troops. V-1 was essentially a jet-propelled, aerial torpedo with wings, and not a true rocket.

To escape aerial reconnaissance and bombing, the assembly of V-1's and V-2's was transferred in the fall of 1943 from Peenemünde to the Mittelwerke, a huge factory underneath the Harz Mountains, near Nordhausen. Above is the entrance to one of the two main tunnels captured by the U. S. 3rd Armored Division in early April 1945. Partially completed V-2's are shown inside the tunnel below.

Dornberger (on left) and von Braun (with cast) on May 3, 1945, at Reutte, in the Austrian Tyrol, shortly after they were taken by units of the 44th Infantry Division, U. S. Seventh Army.

Fourteen tons of documents relating to V-2 were buried in an abandoned German mine. They were discovered by Major Robert Staver of U. S. Army Ordnance. Here, Staver (left), Karl Otto Fleischer (center), general business manager of the German rocket program, and Walther Riedel, chief designer at Peenemünde, prepare the V-2 documents for shipment from the mine in May 1945 to the U.S.A.

Fort Bliss, Texas, March 1946: From left to right Major James P. Hamill, who played a key role in evacuating V-2's to the United States; Colonel Holger N. Toftoy, Chief, Rocket Branch, U. S. Army Ordnance, and Wernher von Braun, then a "Department of the Army Special Employee."

*Courtesy Major General H. N. Toftoy, U.S.A. (Ret.)*

Colonel Hamill (left), von Braun (center), and Major General Toftoy hold a reunion at Huntsville, Alabama, shortly after von Braun and his team succeeded in boosting America's first satellite, Explorer I, into orbit on January 31, 1958.

*Courtesy Major General H. N. Toftoy, U.S.A. (Ret.)*

*Public Information Office, George C. Marshall Space Flight Center NASA, Huntsville, Alab.*

October 1962, and Wernher von Braun (right), director of the civilian George C. Marshall Space Flight Center at Huntsville, Alabama, stands before a Saturn rocket, with Dr. Kurt Debus, Director of the NASA Launch Operations Directorate at Cape Kennedy. Dr. Debus also began his career at Peenemünde, where he was in charge of test firing the V-2.

Welborn and Lovelady allowed themselves to be led to the entrance of a large tunnel from which rails led directly into a mountainside. They saw, stacked up near trucks and freight cars at the tunnel entrance, some long, slender objects with four fins and radioed for Major William Castille, Combat Command "B's" Military Intelligence officer. The three Americans then entered the tunnel and quickly realized that they had come upon the underground factory where the V-weapons had been manufactured.

Major Castille recalls that the tour "was like being in a magician's cave." There were two tunnels running parallel to each other for slightly more than a mile into the mountainside. Here V-1 and V-2 parts were arranged in orderly rows. Cross tunnels were filled with precision machinery and tools. Telephone, ventilating, and lighting systems were still in operation. The huge subterranean complex had not been damaged and appeared to have been abandoned in perfect working order by its German guards and technicians. Castille left the *Mittelwerke* and sent word of the find back to Military Intelligence headquarters in Paris, which in turn notified the Army Ordnance units which had expressed interest in the V-weapon targets.

On the south side of the *Mittelwerke*, Castille, Welborn, and Lovelady made another, sickening discovery: the Dora concentration camp. Prisoners from the Nordhausen camp had been marched to work in the *Mittelwerke* each morning at 4 A.M., but Dora was part of the factory itself. Swarms of half-crazed, starving slave laborers greeted the arrival of the American tankers with hysterical joy. Five men tried to lift Lieutenant Herbert Gontard to their shoulders, but they were so weak that they couldn't do it. Medical units were rushed into Dora. On litters and in ambulances, thousands of inmates were brought out of the camp to improvised hospitals. The Engineers came in with bulldozers and dug mass graves for the hundreds of naked corpses which had been dumped on the ground in front of the crematoriums. In the chaos caused by the American approach, the SS had fled and failed to carry out Hans Kammler's instructions to destroy the human evidence of Nordhausen and Dora.

The next day, April 12, the 3rd Armored left the Nordhausen area in control of the 104th Infantry Division and drove eastward toward Sangerhausen and the Saale River. Remembering the two slave-labor camps, "the tankers of the 3rd were in a savage mood as they went on to the final battles."

News that the *Mittelwerke* was in the hands of the Timberwolf Division was passed on to Colonel Holger Toftoy, Chief of Ordnance Technical Intelligence in Paris, who had been asked in March to ship one hundred V-2's to White Sands, New Mexico, by Colonel Trichel, Chief of the Rocket Branch in the Pentagon. Colonel Toftoy had not been able to find any operational V-2's because the Germans had fired them as soon as they were brought to the launching areas. Now, however, the Americans—and the Americans alone— were in possession of a whole factory of V-2's.

The job of bringing them out of the chaos of central Germany with the war still on, over clogged roads or bomb-shattered railway lines to the crowded port of Antwerp, presented formidable problems. Given the fact of American control of the *Mittelwerke* and its surrounding territory, however, Colonel Toftoy had no reason to believe, in late April 1945, that the complex evacuation could not be accomplished in orderly fashion. Though occupied with scores of other weapon projects, he began planning the V-2 evacuation on a priority basis.

In London, Major Robert Staver, who had been sent to Europe by Colonel Trichel to direct the location and interrogation of the German rocket specialists, learned that the *Mittelwerke* had been taken and that he could now begin to accomplish his assignment. On April 20 he flew to Paris Ordnance Headquarters. It was Staver's intention to move up to the Nordhausen area as soon as he could obtain clearance. While waiting for it to be declared a noncombat zone, he sent the civilian engineers from Project Hermes to targets in areas that had been officially cleared of all enemy resistance.

Staver was determined to go to Nordhausen even though he had received the following report, again from British Intelligence:

| | |
|---|---|
| CIOS NO: | 4/149 |
| PRIORITY: | 1 |
| LOCATION: | About 10 km. SW of Garmisch-Partenkirchen (Tyrol) |
| ACTIVITY: | Rocket and guided missile research and development |
| PERSONNEL: | Prof. Dr. Wernher Freiherr von Braun<br>Dir. Riedel<br>Dr. Demant or Dcmanz<br>Head Ing. Ludewig      see 4/95 for other names |
| REMARKS: | Reliably reported that most important part of Peenemünde Research Establishment (4/95) evacuated to this location. Excavations in mountainside close to lake for underground workshop.[1] |

Staver had placed von Braun's name at the top of his Black List, and he was disappointed to learn that the technical director of the V-2 program and some of his key associates had left central Germany for Bavaria. This sudden departure, however, did not reduce Nordhausen as the primary target. Staver reasoned that a large concentration of rocket specialists, and probably the V-2 documents, must have been left behind in Nordhausen, which was now under firm American control. The Bavarian Alps, four hundred miles away, were also in a zone marked out for occupation by American troops, but Staver had reason to believe that this event might be months away.

The American military leaders were taking at face value repeated reports that the Führer and leading Nazis were planning a last-ditch stand in the mountains of Bavaria and western Austria. On March 11, General Eisenhower himself had been informed by a top-secret intelligence report that the Germans were preparing a mountain stronghold in the Alpine Zone which was, "by the very nature of the terrain, practically impenetrable." The report continued:

> Here, defended by nature and by the most efficient secret weapons yet invented, the powers that have hitherto guided Germany will survive to reorganize her resurrection; here armaments will be manufactured in bombproof factories, food and equipment will be stored in vast underground caverns and specially selected corps of young men will be trained in guerrilla warfare, so that a whole underground army can be fitted and directed to liberate Germany from the occupying forces.[2]

General Bedell Smith, Eisenhower's chief of staff, seriously considered that "a prolonged campaign," producing heavy casualties, might be necessary to take the Alpine Redoubt. In the face of this kind of high-level thinking, Major Staver could not be expected to believe that American troops were likely in the near future to secure the area where many German rocket specialists were now reported to be working. And even after it was captured, the rocket men had one of the finest natural hideouts in Europe in the dense forests, scattered, isolated villages, and icy crags of the Austro-Bavarian Alps. A game of hide-and-seek could be played there indefinitely. Staver decided to go to Nordhausen, where he was certain that there were rocket targets that had been secured by First Army T-Forces. Then after American troops had stormed the Alpine fortress, he could continue his investigations in the mountains.

Major Staver was wise in not wanting to lose any time in

reaching Nordhausen. British and Soviet Intelligence, of course, were after the same V-2 targets that he was, although there seemed to be very little they could do about taking them away from the Americans. However, Staver realized that his most serious immediate competition might come from other branches of the American armed forces. Technical teams from the United States Navy and Army Air Forces were active in Germany and might dispute Army Ordnance's claim to the V-2 targets. The investigation of scientific intelligence targets had become a high-priority, competitive undertaking.

The Army Air Forces Scientific Advisory Group, a top-secret project formed by General Henry H. Arnold and headed by Professor Theodore von Kármán, had already turned up a fantastic amount of information on new German aerodynamic developments. When Major General Hugh J. Knerr, Deputy Commanding General for Administration of the U. S. Strategic Air Forces in Europe, grasped what von Kármán and his team were uncovering, he had written to Lieutenant General Carl Spaatz, commanding USSTAF, in March 1945: "Occupation of German scientific and industrial establishments has revealed the fact that we have been alarmingly backward in many fields of research. If we do not take this opportunity to seize the apparatus and the brains that developed it and put this combination back to work promptly, we will remain several years behind while we attempt to cover a field already exploited." [3]

When Robert Lovett, Assistant Secretary of War for Air, visited the European Theater in early April 1945, General Knerr had urged him to press upon the War Department a plan not just for interrogating captured German scientists but for actually bringing them to the United States to resume their work. Knerr had recommended that the scientists' families be brought, too, "not only for the mental stability it would give the men to know they are safe," but to prevent the Russians from using the families as hostages in the scientists' absence.

Knerr's recommendation was not acted upon immediately, but it did put a different cast upon scientific intelligence investigations. The War Department began to study the feasibility of an operation that was unique in American history: the wholesale importation of captured enemy scientists. Their expertise would be used in the war against Japan, which seemed likely to continue long after the European war had ended. This also would deny their knowledge to the Soviet Union.

That such planning was being considered in Washington, of course, could not be known by investigators in Europe such as Major Staver, and would not affect their actions until late June.

The War Department knew that the Russians had been too heavily engaged in fighting to have been able to undertake long-range development programs. In 1945 the Soviet Union—although it had stolen the secret of the atom bomb from its allies, a fact the latter were unaware of—had no big rockets, jet planes, or electric-powered submarines. The Germans had all three, and it was obvious that Soviet Intelligence was engaged in a thorough search for these and other inventions.

A special committee under the Council of People's Commissars, headed by Malenkov, had, in fact, been formed in late 1944. Representatives of VIAM, the All-Union Institute of Aviation Materials; TSAGI, the Central Aerodynamics and Hydrodynamics Institute; NISO, the Scientific Research Institute for Airplane Equipment; and engineers from various other commissariats had been given special powers and a mission. Armed with lists of names and installations, they were to follow the Red Army and the Secret Police into Hungary, Rumania, Czechoslovakia, Austria, and Germany. Stalin put in a claim for ten billion dollars' worth of reparations, including German scientific establishments, at Yalta in February 1945, and the technical teams were assigned to collect.[4]

As far as the German long-range rocket and the specialists who had produced it were concerned, it appeared in April 1945 that in view of the American occupation of the Harz Mountain area the Russians were going to be as frustrated in central Germany as they had been at Blizna in southern Poland and at Peenemünde. Major Staver, of course, could have no specific knowledge of Soviet intentions, but he suspected that the Russians would not abandon their interest in the V-2 targets, even though they were in American hands. He also sensed that competition might arise from the British. It was with a heightened sense of urgency, therefore, that Staver prepared to go to Nordhausen to carry out his mission for Army Ordnance and Colonel Trichel.

In view of the report he had received that von Braun and many of his key men were in the Alps, however, Staver took the precaution of leaving a message for Dr. Richard Porter at Paris Ordnance Headquarters. The latter was the leader of the civilian General Electric Project Hermes team which had been made available in Europe to Major Staver.

Dr. Porter was thirty-two years old. Born in Salina, Kansas, he had taken his B.S. at the University of Kansas in 1934 and his doctorate in electrical engineering at Yale in 1937. When General Electric chose him to lead Project Hermes, he was regarded as one of the most brilliant young scientists in the United States and had been chiefly responsible for the electronic central fire-control system on the B-29 bomber. While waiting for the V-2 target areas to be opened up by combat units, Dr. Porter and his Project Hermes team[5] were busy investigating other guided-missile targets in territory under American control to which Staver had assigned them.

According to Staver's calculations, Dr. Porter was somewhere near the University of Heidelberg. He would, however, return to Paris after completing this investigation. Staver wanted him to be alerted to the report that many of the key rocket men were now in the Bavarian Alps. If American troops should succeed in opening up the area more quickly than anyone thought possible, Dr. Porter was instructed to drop all other Black List investigations immediately and attempt to locate for interrogation Dr. von Braun and his associates.

# 11

## Man on a bicycle

On April 4, 1945, Wernher von Braun arrived in Oberammergau. This quiet village of woodcarvers and old brightly painted peasants' houses, with a tiny green river running through its center, had been completely untouched by the war. It was possible to believe in this picture-postcard setting that nothing had happened in the world since the first Passion Play had been given in Oberammergau in 1634.

Von Braun, however, was brought back to reality as he quickly noted two facts. Oberammergau lay in the heart of the Alpine Redoubt, the supposed mountain fortress. But there was nothing there that could offer more than minimal resistance to a determined attacker. The Alpine Redoubt was, in fact, a fantasy, the last great propaganda effort of Dr. Goebbels. But if there was no formidable concentration of troops and weapons to be seen around Oberammergau, the SS, at least, was present in force. The *Elektromechanische Werke* engineers were quartered in a camp that had once housed an Alpine regiment. The *Kaserne* was comfortable, with a sweeping view of the Ammer Valley and the snow-capped Alps, but it was surrounded by barbed wire and guarded by men of the SD. "Kammler's gang," as the rocket men referred to their unwanted protectors, was in complete charge.

Upon arriving at the camp, von Braun set himself two tasks. The first was to carry out further rocket research while there was still time. He was gratified to discover that the Peenemünde wind tunnel was in operation at nearby Kochel. This wind tunnel, one of the few—and certainly the most advanced—in the world at the time, had been moved all the way to the Bavarian mountains from Peenemünde after the R.A.F. air raid of August 17, 1943. Some other equipment also had recently been brought up from Nordhausen by truck and train. And of course the five hundred engineers in Oberammergau could further their work simply by using pencils and paper. As for the V-2 documents, von Braun now knew they were safely hidden and where. Huzel and Tessmann had arrived in Oberammergau and confided this secret to him. In Nordhausen itself, only one man knew where the documents were located. This was Karl Otto Fleischer, the commercial director (roughly, general business manager) of EW. Fleischer had been told of the Dörnten hiding place before Huzel and Tessmann themselves had left for the Alps.

Von Braun's second task was to discover what was going on in SS General Kammler's mind. Von Braun suspected that Kammler had concentrated the EW engineers within the barbed wire of the former Army camp in order to use them as hostages when the Americans approached. But von Braun could not be certain of this. In any case, Kammler had been nowhere in evidence during von Braun's first week in Oberammergau. Then one evening the Special Commissioner suddenly sent for him.

Von Braun discovered that Kammler had set up temporary headquarters in "the house of Jesus Christ," as the Hotel Alois Lang was referred to locally. Lang was an innkeeper who played Christ in the Passion Play (later, a denazification court would determine that the only member of the cast who had not been a party member was the man who played Judas).

As von Braun waited in the lobby of the hotel to be summoned into the presence of the Special Commissioner, he overheard a conversation between Kammler and his chief of staff, SS Major Starck, who were in the next room, the tavern. Three miles south of Oberammergau, in Ettal, was a large fourteenth-century abbey and rococo abbey church. It was here that Benedictine monks distilled the renowned *Ettaler Klosterlikör*, a special liqueur made from a secret formula that was highly popular in Germany.

As von Braun remembers it, his first thought was that Kammler and Starck were obviously enjoying their share of Ettaler Klosterlikör. They were discussing various ways of evading the approaching Allies. None of them seemed promising. Then von Braun recalls Starck offering Kammler a suggestion that struck von Braun, at least, as unique and more than a little startling: Kammler was advised to burn his uniform, don civilian clothing, enter the Ettal monastery, and pose as a monk.

Kammler, with all his faults, was not noted for any lack of a sense of humor. Von Braun heard him reply that the suggestion indeed had merit; the monastery was a perfect hideout and there were at least plenty to drink on the premises. He might be of use to the monks in managing the commercial end of their liqueur operation and might well make a future career out of this.

Von Braun had begun to wonder whether Kammler was indulging himself in irony or really taking this bizarre idea of entering the Ettal monastery seriously when an SS guard asked him to step into the tavern adjoining the lobby. Von Braun recalls noting that Starck, with a machine pistol resting against his right leg, was sitting next to Kammler. The Special Commissioner, however, was in a genial mood.

Whether it was because of the Ettaler Klosterlikör or relief at having evaded the American tanks approaching Nordhausen, he had lost his haggard, wild-eyed look.

With his broad shoulders, bronzed clear-cut features, and quick wit, Hans Kammler could be a captivating personality when it suited him, and it seemed to suit him now. In a disarming way he offered von Braun a glass of liqueur, asked him to sit down, and expressed concern about his peaked look and broken arm and shoulder. He had sent for the technical director of EW, Kammler said, to ask him whether he and his engineers were being well taken care of and were resuming their all-important research work for the future. When informed that this was indeed the case, Kammler seemed pleased and said that his post as General Commissioner for Turbojet Fighters would require him to leave Oberammergau for an indeterminate period. He was turning over the local command to SS Major Kummer. He hoped that von Braun and the other technical people would cooperate with Kummer as they had with him. Final victory was still attainable, he said. That was all. Professor von Braun could go.

As he walked back to the barracks, von Braun found himself more baffled than ever by Kammler's intentions. He considered the man a glib charlatan but far from unintelligent. Could he really believe in the final victory and the Alpine Redoubt? If not, did he seriously think he could get away with hiding in a monastery? Or did he, as von Braun suspected, realize that the end was near and intend to use the rocket engineers as hostages? Whatever Kammler had in mind, von Braun decided that his engineers must be gotten out of that tight little barracks area where they were completely at the mercy of the SD.

The next day he verified that Kammler had left Oberammergau. None of the officers of his staff knew or would say where he had gone. Von Braun and his old friend Dr. Ernst

Steinhoff, the EW director of guidance and control, discussed the problem of getting engineers out of the barracks area and came up with a solution they thought might work. They went to see Major Kummer and found him to be a pale copy of Kammler. He was polite, genial, handsome, but lacked the Special Commissioner's drive and native shrewdness. Sensing a certain uneasiness in Kummer, caused perhaps by the weight of his new responsibilities, von Braun and Steinhoff decided to play their hunch. First they told the SS major that they appreciated the importance of his assignment. Then they emphasized that the Americans, of course, would not succeed in breaking into the Alpine Redoubt which all of them knew was impregnable. Still, one had to face up to the fact that until the new jets could clear the skies the American Air Force would continue to bomb and strafe at will. Suppose one of their *Jabos* should drop a bomb in the middle of the barracks? Most of the engineers, who were responsible for the Third Reich's greatest technical achievement, would be killed. These men were now Major Kummer's direct responsibility. How would he explain their loss to Kammler and SS Headquarters?

Kummer thought this over for a while. Then, as von Braun remembers it, a flight of *Jabos*—P-47 Thunderbolts—suddenly whined overhead. Just as suddenly, Kummer's attitude changed from one of skeptical indecision to conciliatory. He admitted that von Braun and Steinhoff had a valid point but wondered what he could do about it.

Simply move the men out of the barracks, they told him, into neighboring villages. Scatter them so that no single bombing attack could wipe them all out.

Kummer found this a worthwhile suggestion but replied that it could not be executed; he lacked the necessary transportation. When Steinhoff said that many trucks and cars assigned to EW in Nordhausen had been driven to the Alps, Kummer said he had very little gasoline and what little there was at his disposal could not be used to move civilians.

Steinhoff persisted. There was a good deal of fuel for rocket motors available, liquid oxygen and alcohol. Given a small amount of gasoline, he could come up with a mixture that would be adequate to power trucks and cars. Kummer considered this proposal for what von Braun remembers as an agonizingly long time; then, as the American *Jabos* flew overhead again, he agreed to it.

The five hundred EW engineers were moved out of the former Army camp in Oberammergau and billeted in twenty-five surrounding villages. They were, however, accompanied by SD men. The threat of their being held as hostages or murdered by some of the more fanatical Nazis as the American approached remained to haunt von Braun. But the threat had diminished considerably; the SD could no longer treat the rocket men as a malleable unit.

Von Braun himself moved to Weilheim, a village twenty miles south of Oberammergau, and took quarters in a small house in a government housing development with his younger brother, Magnus, who had been in charge of gyroscope mass production at Nordhausen. By this time, lack of sleep, overwork, constant travel, anxiety over the intentions of the SS, and the pain in his left arm and shoulder, which had not been properly set after his automobile accident, had brought von Braun to the verge of collapse. He would have to do something about his arm, he knew, or risk losing it. He entered a hospital at nearby Sonthofen and placed himself under the care of a surgeon noted for repairing the broken and fractured bones of mountain climbers and skiers.

Von Braun, who was unknown to the German public, was just another patient to the surgeon, who cut off his plaster cast and rebroke his arm and shoulder. There were no anaesthetics because they were in short supply and could be administered only to those who absolutely had to have them. The surgeon advised von Braun that, if complete recovery was expected, a second operation would be necessary, after which he could be fitted with a better cast. The overworked surgeon would try to get back to Professor von Braun in three or four days; meanwhile, he was ordered to remain in bed in traction and not to attempt any movement.

The next day the American *Jabos* put in an appearance over Sonthofen, bombing and strafing the town. Von Braun lay rigid on his metal cot as the bombs fell so close to the hospital that patients rated as serious cases were hurriedly moved to the basement. The basement was small and soon overcrowded. Von Braun was left in his room. The *Jabos* departed after an attack lasting half an hour. They did not hit the hospital. Von Braun remembers their visit as being less nerve-racking than not knowing what was going on in the world beyond Sonthofen. The war was obviously coming to an end, but his sole source of information about it was the *Deutschlandsender*, the government radio station, which could not be relied upon for an accurate picture of events.

On that April 20, 1945, the Russians were in the suburbs of Berlin. It was Hitler's fifty-sixth birthday, and the Führer celebrated it quietly fifty feet underground in the Chancellery air-raid shelter. It had been Hitler's intention to move south to the Alpine Redoubt on April 20, but instead he ordered an all-out attack on the Russians who were ringing Berlin. The attack was never launched, because there were no forces left to fight effectively. Hitler remained in Berlin, although Goering and some of the various commands and ministries did reach the Alps.

The Russians were in almost complete control of eastern Germany (they were also only a few miles from the von Braun family estate in Silesia, where Baron von Braun and his wife were living). In the west, the British-Canadian armies were sweeping over the north German plain and the

United States First Army had reached the Elbe River near Magdeburg, eighty miles from Berlin. In five days, Russian and American units would meet at the Elbe, cutting northern and southern Germany in half.

On April 16 the American Seventh Army had reached Nuremberg and General Eisenhower made a decision. Increasingly concerned by intelligence reports on the Alpine Redoubt, he directed Patch's Seventh Army to shift its line of advance toward southern Bavaria and the Tyrol, seize the Munich-Augsburg area, clear the sector north of the Swiss border, and advance into Austria to link up with the U. S. Fifth Army driving up from Italy. The French First Army was directed to cross the Danube near Ulm and drive toward Lake Constance and the Alpine Redoubt, which the French began to do with great speed and efficiency.

Von Braun, of course, had no way of knowing that both French and American units were engaging in a race to reach the supposed Alpine Redoubt. He could not know that counter-intelligence officers in the forward units of both armies had been alerted to be on the lookout for the EW rocket engineers and, if they were found, to hold them for interrogation by rear-echelon scientific intelligence units. He did not know that his name was on the Black List and that Major Robert Staver, in Nordhausen, was attempting to track down the V-2 documents and the V-2 specialists who had not been sent to the Alps. He did not know, as he lay rigid on the hospital cot, that the Americans were at that very time organizing a mission to ship one hundred V-2's from the *Mittelwerke* to a testing ground in New Mexico.

As the days passed and rumors that the French were approaching spread through the hospital, von Braun's principal concern was simply survival. He was helpless. There was nothing to prevent the SD from entering the hospital, taking him away for use as a hostage, or murdering him to prevent his talents from being used by the Allies. The latter possibility, given the chaotic conditions of the time and the state of mind of some of the more fanatic Nazis, was one that could not be taken lightly.

Around April 25, von Braun roused himself from his first good sleep in five days to find a uniformed figure looming over his bed. He remembers that his first reaction was one of fear, until he saw that the intruder was not wearing SS black but the gray-green of the Army and a Red Cross armband.

The soldier said that he had an ambulance and orders to drive Professor von Braun to Oberjoch. Still wary, von Braun asked the soldier who had sent him. General Dornberger, the soldier replied. Von Braun was to dress and accompany him immediately because there were reports that the French were closing in on the Sonthofen hospital.

The surgeon was sent for and expertly applied a new plaster cast on Von Braun's torso and left arm, the latter suspended horizontally across his chest. The surgeon was opposed to von Braun's leaving the hospital and warned him that if he expected his arm and shoulder to heal properly he would need complete rest for at least a month, with as little movement as possible.

Von Braun said he would attempt to heed this advice, then followed the soldier downstairs to the waiting ambulance. They raced through the valley of the Ostrach for five miles until they reached the village of Hindelang on the frontier of the Austrian Tyrol. Then the driver slowed to take the curves leading up to Oberjoch, a small Alpine summer resort and winter sports center boasting Kneipp, sauna, mud baths, and a ski lift.

Von Braun saw no sports enthusiasts or vacationers in the picturesque streets of the tiny resort, but as the ambulance stopped before Haus Ingeborg, a large three-story hotel with a sloping roof, he did see hurrying toward him a dozen men in gray leather overcoats. Leading them was General Dornberger, followed by von Braun's younger brother, Magnus, and some of the old Peenemünde engineers. They pumped von Braun's good hand, greeted him effusively, and led him into the brightly lit hotel lobby, which was crowded with civilian technicians and soldiers in uniform.

Von Braun remembers thinking that General Dornberger couldn't have picked a better hideout than this hotel. It seemed to rest on the roof of the world. His relief at being out of the Sonthofen hospital and back among old friends, however, soon turned to anxiety. Mingling with the Army soldiers in the lobby, he saw a large number of SD men and asked Dornberger if Kammler was present. No one seemed to know what had happened to the Special Commissioner, replied Dornberger, who had brought his military staff and some of the Peenemünde engineers up to this isolated mountain resort because he wanted to get as far away as he could from the main SS force at Oberammergau. He had not, however, been able to shake a thirty-man SD commando, and as a result the first days in the beautiful surroundings of Haus Ingeborg had been tense, even without the presence of Hans Kammler. Dornberger had foreseen a pitched battle between his own soldiers, who numbered about one hundred, and the SD, if the latter started anything. To avert this, he had invited the leader of the SD commando to his room one night and had slowly but thoroughly gotten him drunk.

Dornberger had asked the officer, a major, for the exact nature of his orders after opening a third bottle of Asbach Uralt. The major replied that his orders were to protect the rocket men.

"Protect us from what?" Dornberger asked.

"From the French and the Americans," the major answered.

"You think that your thirty men can hold off the French and American armies?"

"If we can't do that, my orders are to have all of you shot to prevent your falling into the enemy's hands."

Dornberger remembers feeling a slight chill at that admission and then asking the major if he really thought that the execution of these orders would serve any useful purpose. The war and the SS were finished. One of the Allies would be in Oberjoch in a few days, and they would almost certainly hang the man responsible for murdering a group of civilians. The major took a long pull at the bottle and then suddenly broke down into sobs. Looking at him with piteous contempt, Dornberger realized that he was not dealing with a determined fanatic like Kammler but with a maudlin, guilt-ridden weakling worried about his own skin. He clapped the major on the back and told him that he, General Dornberger, had a plan that would at least save the lives of the SD commando. They were to turn their weapons over to the soldiers, burn their own uniforms, and then put on Army uniforms which Dornberger would provide. When the French of the Americans broke into Oberjoch, they would think that the SD men were ordinary *Wehrmacht* soldiers. They would be sent to a prisoner-of-war camp rather than being shot.

The major limply agreed, and the next day his men turned over their weapons under the watchful eye of General Dornberger, who took great satisfaction in the deal he had pulled off, especially when he told himself that no change of uniform could hide SS tattoos from the diligent investigator. As a result of the general's improvisation, the SD men von Braun had seen in the hotel lobby were no longer a problem. There were only the approaching Allies to worry about.

The future looked bleak. Dornberger had been able to collect only a handful of the old Peenemünde team at Oberjoch; hundreds were still scattered in villages around

Oberammergau, and forty-five hundred had remained in Nordhausen-Bleicherode. The general had once directed seventeen thousand people at Peenemünde, of whom some five thousand were skilled technicians and engineers. This talented organization had been dispersed forever. Now, in April 1945, all he could be certain of was that he and von Braun, who had started out together in Berlin in 1932 and were the two men most responsible for V-2, were still together. Dornberger, a rugged career soldier and hardheaded engineer, also had the sensitivity to grasp the weirdness of the situation:

> About us towered the snow-covered Allgäu mountains, their peaks glittering in the sunlight under the clear blue sky. Far below us it was already spring. The hill pastures were a bright green. Even on our high mountain pass the first flowers were thrusting buds through the melting snow. It was so infinitely peaceful here! Had the last few years been nothing but a bad dream? [1]

The old Peenemünde hands at Oberjoch played chess, talked through the night about rockets and space travel, walked mountain paths for exercise, and worried about the future and the fate of their families left behind in the battle zone of central Germany. They had no way of knowing what was really going on beyond the peaceful Allgäu Mountains but could sense from the radio and the sight of refugees and motorized military units streaming along the highway a hundred yards below Haus Ingeborg that the end was near. But how near? That was the constant and agonizing question.

Wild rumors broke the tense monotony of the wait. One story warned that a horde of Moroccan *goums,* French colonial troops with a reputation for barbarity, particularly when drunk, were moving up the pass from Hindelang and would soon sweep with abandon through Haus Ingeborg.

Upon hearing this story, the owner of the hotel, who until then had maintained with Bavarian stubbornness that the only liquor he could offer his penniless guests was hard cider, now frantically admitted that his cellars concealed a cache of fine wines. Thousands of bottles of champagne and the choicest Rhines and Moselles were hurriedly dispatched by a water-bucket brigade and trucks to the nearest military hospital, out of reach of the oncoming *goums*.

By the next morning, May 1, 1945, there was not a drop of alcohol in Haus Ingeborg. There were no Moroccans, either. They had not stormed up the pass leading to the hotel because they were nowhere near it. The only thing of consequence that happened on May 1 was a radio announcement toward evening. Von Braun, Dornberger, and everyone else in Haus Ingeborg gathered around the radio as a long roll of military drums interrupted Bruckner's Seventh Symphony. Then an announcer said:

> Our Führer, Adolf Hitler, fighting to the last breath against Bolshevism, fell for Germany this afternoon in his operational headquarters in the Reich Chancellery.*

Von Braun recalls waiting for the announcer to continue with details of Germany's capitulation. They were not forthcoming, only the news that Hitler had appointed Grand Admiral Doenitz to be his successor in carrying on the struggle. With Hitler dead, however, von Braun realized that the Third Reich was as good as dead, too, and he determined to salvage something important from its demise. What Peenemünde had accomplished must not perish with the Third Reich, and von Braun reconsidered in earnest his plan to preserve the long-range rocket for the future.

In January 1945, at Peenemünde, when he realized that

---

* This was the official radio announcement. Hitler, of course, had committed suicide a day earlier with the Red Army in almost complete control of Berlin.

the military situation was hopeless, von Braun had held a secret meeting with a score of his closest and most trusted associates. They had discussed the eventual feasibility of surrendering the development team intact to one of the four Allies, the one who would make the best use of it. They did not want to fall into the hands of the Russians under any circumstances, and they reasoned that neither Britain nor France could afford the massive long-range program they envisioned. That left America, a country of Western culture, yet innocent of the ancient grudges that enveloped Germany, France, and England; a new world that had the resources and might have the drive and the imagination to launch a big rocket program leading to space exploration.

In making the choice to leave Peenemünde for Nordhausen, and then in heading up to the Alps, always in the path of the American Army, von Braun had kept his plan within the realm of the possible. Now the time had come to put it into effect. He would voluntarily surrender himself and those of his men who were at Oberjoch to the Americans in the hope that the work of Peenemünde would be transferred across the seas and resumed there.

Von Braun broached this idea to Dornberger, whose position as an officer still on active duty was different from that of the civilian engineers. But the general, who had undergone a series of frustrations and humiliations at the hands of the SS and Nazi bureaucrats, saw no point in hesitating until the Third Reich was officially dead. "I agree with you, Wernher," he said. "It's our obligation to put our baby into the right hands."

But how to do it? Remaining at Haus Ingeborg was risky. The hotel might be captured by French troops or occupied by bands of fanatical, die-hard SS who were still roaming through the Austro-Bavarian mountains, killing both Allied soldiers and Germans whom they suspected of wanting to surrender. The rocket men would have to take the initiative and establish direct contact with the Americans. General Dornberger, however, spoke no English, and while Wernher von Braun had studied the language in school, he was not completely fluent. But Magnus von Braun had been studying English intensively and had a good command of it. So early on the morning of May 2, 1945, with fighting still in progress in the Alpine Zone, Wernher von Braun gave his twenty-six-year-old brother a set of instructions.

On that same day a special U.S. Army Ordnance team was reconnoitering the *Mittelwerke* in Nordhausen, four hundred miles away, with the purpose of transporting one hundred V-2's from the underground factory to the port of Antwerp. Major Robert Staver, in the same area, was attempting to locate the V-2 documents and the rocket specialists who had not gone to the Alps. British, Soviet, and American intelligence officers attached to advanced combat units of their respective armies had been instructed to be on the alert for any sign of Wernher von Braun, Walter Dornberger, and the other key figures who had produced V-2. None of these intelligence officers had the slightest clue as to the exact location of their targets as Magnus von Braun walked out of Haus Ingeborg and seated himself upon a bicycle.

Munich had fallen to the United States Seventh Army on April 30, and its divisions rolled beyond the Bavarian capital to the perimeter of the Alpine Redoubt, expecting a full-scale battle from a band of Nazi fanatics. But while there was some scattered resistance from the German Fifteenth Army, the principal barrier to American progress turned out to be the traffic jams on the Alpine roads.

The Seventh Army's 44th Infantry Division, which had seen heavy fighting in France, drove all the way to Reutte in the Austrian Tyrol, bypassing Oberjoch and Hindelang on the German side of the border. But one of its units, the anti-tank company of the 324th Infantry Regiment, was patrolling this remote area on the morning of May 2. To the west, a few hours away, were lead elements of the First French Army, which had successfully skirted Lake Constance.

The men of the anti-tank company made their way cautiously down a lonely, silent country road, on the lookout for trouble from the deep snowy woods towering above them on either side. The soldiers tensed as they watched a figure approaching, then saw that it was only a lone civilian on a bike, pedaling toward them out of a gray haze. He was young, blond, wore a gray leather overcoat, and was unarmed. He came up to Fred Schneiker, a private first class from Sheboygan, Wisconsin, who acted as the company's interpreter, and told him that his name was Magnus von Braun and that his brother, Wernher, and many of the men responsible for V-2 were in a hotel a hundred yards ahead and wanted to surrender to the Americans.

Schneiker had heard about V-2, but he knew only that it was a big rocket. Nobody had briefed him or any of the other combat men on any intelligence objectives concerning it. It just did not seem possible to PFC Schneiker that the men who had produced V-2 were a few minutes away and wanted to give themselves up. "I think you're nuts," Schneiker is reported to have told Magnus von Braun, voicing the feelings of the other soldiers, "but we'll investigate."

Not wanting to run the risk that Magnus von Braun's story was designed to lead it into an ambush, the anti-tank company did not investigate by advancing up to Haus Ingeborg. Instead, PFC Schneiker brought Magnus down to the 44th Division's Counter-Intelligence Corps headquarters in Reutte. It was CIC's job to check on such stories in front-line areas. CIC, however, was not qualified to conduct complicated technical interrogations. It was somewhat taken aback by von Braun's story but was nevertheless aware that a plan existed for interrogating captured German scientists in depth. After lengthy questioning, CIC gave Magnus von Braun safe-conduct passes, told him to go back to his hotel and to return with these men who were supposed to have invented V-2.

Magnus von Braun reached Haus Ingeborg at two o'clock of an overcast afternoon. His brother listened to his report, examined his safe-conduct passes, and then ordered three field-gray passenger sedans readied for the trip. In addition to the drivers, seven men got into the cars, which had been jammed with their personal belongings: Wernher and Magnus von Braun; General Dornberger and his chief of staff, Lieutenant Colonel Herbert Axster, who had been an attorney in civilian life; Hans Lindenberg, a combustion-chamber engineer; and Bernhard Tessmann and Dieter Huzel, the two engineers who had hidden the V-2 documents in the Dörnten mine. It was a forlorn convoy that moved down the Adolf Hitler Pass in the rain, almost two years to the day that Duncan Sandys had begun his investigation of German secret weapon development. For Germany, the story of V-2, the weapon which could have changed the course of the war had it been ready for use in 1942, was now over. Neither Dornberger nor von Braun could know what the future held for them or what kind of reception they would receive from American combat troops.

The rocket specialists were met in Schattwald by jeeps and escorted the rest of the way into Reutte, which was reached after dark. At Reutte, they were questioned by German-speaking CIC soldiers and then assigned rooms in a requisitioned house. The next morning they were given an American breakfast. Wernher von Braun was given no cause to regret his decision to surrender to the Americans and was relieved at the treatment his group received. "They didn't kick me in the teeth or anything," he later remarked. "They just fried me some eggs."

On May 5 the German armies north of the Alps surren-

dered. When the Third Reich itself surrendered uncondi-
tionally at 2:41 on the morning of May 7, von Braun and
Dornberger had been moved from Reutte. Counter-Intelligence had rounded up nearly five hundred of the Peenemünde group which had been scattered throughout the Alps
and they, along with the two principal V-2 figures, were in-
carcerated in a large former German military administration
building in Garmisch-Partenkirchen. It was surrounded by
barbed wire and guarded by American soldiers. Garmisch-
Partenkirchen, the site of the 1936 Winter Olympics, nestles
in a wide green valley at the foot of Germany's highest mountain, the Zugspitze. To this splendid resort which had not
been touched by the war came a group of technical investigators representing the interests of the various branches of
the American and British armed services. They found the
five hundred EW men interned at Garmisch willing to talk
about V-2. The bulk of the vast Peenemünde organization,
however, and its equipment remained in Nordhausen, and
the V-2 documents remained buried in the abandoned mine
at Dörnten. In this area of central Germany, Major Staver
was engaged in investigations of his own. Because of the lack
of an efficient communications system between Nordhausen
and Garmisch, Staver had no clear idea of what was going on
in the latter place.

Dr. Richard Porter, however, who was in London on VE-
day (May 8), was notified there that von Braun and his
group had surrendered, and lost no time in moving to Garmisch. Dr. Porter and his General Electric Project Hermes
team wound up conducting the greater part of these early
interrogations for U.S. Army Ordnance, although scores of
other interrogators from other services, both American and
British, were also active.

The primary mission of these men was to find out all they
could about V-2. In the beginning, this press of investigators
and the questions they asked disconcerted General Dorn-

berger. "They didn't know what to ask," he later said. "It was like they were talking Chinese to us!"

Fritz Zwicky, a Bulgarian-born, Swiss-educated astrophysicist who spoke German and was a full professor at the California Institute of Technology, was one of the interrogators representing the Army Air Forces. He later said: "There were too many technical teams, both British and American, the members of which conducted interviews without any coordination with others and with little regard to what had previously been done." Dornberger and the others, Zwicky said, "watched the unexpected and disorderly procedures of the British and American teams with discerning eyes and it became apparent that they considered our missions pretty much of a farce. . . ." [2]

Dornberger and von Braun were playing for bigger stakes. They submitted to the endless interrogations not only because they were prisoners but also because their answers might give their inquisitors the idea that the information was worthy of preservation and of being transferred to another country. Throughout the early period, the group at Garmisch revealed only what Dornberger, his chief of staff, Lieutenant Colonel Axster, and von Braun judged that they should divulge. These men were waiting for the American or British investigators to present some big, long-term proposal before they would tell everything. The investigators, however, were not authorized to perform any function except to ascertain the military history and potential of V-2. Von Braun attempted to suggest that V-2 was more than a weapon. On May 15, 1945, he was asked to write a lengthy report. He entitled it *Survey of Development of Liquid Rockets in Germany and Their Future Prospects,* and wrote:

> We [the Peenemünde team] consider the A-4 stratospheric rocket developed by us (known to the public as V-2) as an intermediate solution conditioned by this war, a solution which still has certain inherent shortcomings, and which com-

pares with the future possibilities of the art about in the same way as a bomber plane of the last war compares with a modern bomber or large passenger plane. We are convinced that a complete mastery of the art of rockets will change conditions in the world in much the same way as did the mastery of aeronautics and that this change will apply both to the civilian and military aspects of their use. We know, on the other hand, from our past experience that a complete mastery of the art is only possible if large sums of money are expended on its development and that setbacks and sacrifices will occur, such as was the case with the development of aircraft. . . .

In the more distant future, the development of rockets offers in our opinion the following possibilities, some of which are of tremendous significance:

(A) Development of long-range commercial planes and long-range bombers of ultra-high speeds. The flight duration of a fast rocket aircraft going from Europe to America would be approximately 40 minutes. . . .

(B) Construction of multi-stage piloted rockets, which would reach a maximum speed of over 7500 meters per second outside the earth's atmosphere. . . .

(C) Instead of having a rocket set up as an "observation platform" outside the earth, it would be possible later on to build a station specially for the purpose, and send the components up into interstellar spaces by means of rockets, to be erected there. . . .

(D) According to a proposal by the German scientist, Professor Oberth, an observation station of this type could be equipped with an enormous mirror, consisting of a huge net of steel wire onto which the metal foils could be suspended. . . . This would enable large towns, for instance, to get sunlight during the evening hours. . . .

(E) When the art of rockets is developed further, it will be possible to go to other planets, first of all to the moon. . . ." [3]

General Dornberger, in a report on rocketry given to the investigators on May 17, 1945, made some predictions that seemed, for the time, as fantastic as von Braun's:

The further possibilities for the future are available: scientific high-altitude rockets, a station in space, travel to the moon and to the stars. . . . That state will be first in space which has the courage to make a clear decision. The stratospheric travel rocket will come as certainly as the modern locomotive followed the Stevenson locomotive. . . .

Dornberger and von Braun, it became obvious to the investigators, were concentrating on the future with these statements and directing their people to cooperate in the hope, as one report put it, "that if they can convince the British and the Americans of the value of their work, there is a chance that facilities may be offered in England or America for continuing it." And, in fact, if an offer of future work was not forthcoming there was nothing to prevent the rocket specialists from clamming up or simply going off to someone who would make them an offer, perhaps the Russians. With the exception of General Dornberger, who could be held as a prisoner of war, the Peenemünde engineers were civilians with no criminal charges against them. There was no legal way to detain them in Garmisch indefinitely. Nor was there any extra-legal way, either, if for no other reason than that this would be frowned upon by Military Government, which was trying to introduce democratic procedures in Germany.

Of the five hundred men originally detained at Garmisch, three hundred of them had, in fact, departed by the second week in May. Some had been interviewed briefly, earmarked for possible future interrogation, and given transportation to their homes; others had simply climbed over the fences and taken off. These people, however, were not considered key figures in the German rocket program. The latter all remained in areas occupied by the United States Army. In early May 1945, it appeared that British, and especially Soviet, Intelligence had been completely shut out in the race for the V-2 targets. At this time, there was no American plan to do anything with the key V-2 personnel beyond interrogating them, and no apparent reason for making a quick decision about their future movements. There was the American plan to ship one hundred V-2's to New Mexico, but here again the Americans seemed to have more than enough time to accomplish their objective in an orderly fashion. The V-2 factory with its rows of machine tools and rocket components was under the firm control of the First Army. The hiding place of the V-2 documents had not been divulged by the Germans, but it was reasoned that this, too, had to be in territory occupied by the Americans and would be discovered in time.

Then suddenly time ran out. The first American objective of evacuating one hundred V-2's from the *Mittelwerke* was thrown into jeopardy. A high-level diplomatic decision put Soviet Intelligence back into the race for the V-2 spoils of war.

# 12

## Special mission V-2

Shortly after learning that Nordhausen had been taken by the 3rd Armored Division on April 11, Colonel Toftoy, in Paris, had organized Special Mission V-2. Its job was to go into the *Mittelwerke* and evacuate from it the hundred V-2's that Colonel Trichel wanted shipped to the White Sands Proving Ground in New Mexico. There seemed to be no particular problems connected with accomplishing this mission.

Then, around April 25, Colonel Toftoy had learned to his considerable surprise and consternation, that as soon as the Third Reich officially surrendered, a vast area of central and eastern Germany—400 miles long and 120 miles at its greatest width—which had been conquered and occupied by American troops would be given to the Russians. All American troops would be withdrawn, and they would be replaced by Red Army units.

The zone in question happened to include Nordhausen, the *Mittelwerke*, all the rocket specialists who had not gone to the Alps with von Braun, and the families of the men who had gone.

The decision to transfer a huge slice of German territory under American control to the Soviet Union, which would put the Russians squarely back into the competition for the V-2 targets and most immediately for the *Mittelwerke,* was the result of lengthy diplomatic negotiations carried out on the highest level by Roosevelt, Churchill, Stalin, and their advisers at the Quebec and Yalta conferences. There were complex and seemingly logical reasons behind it: Eisenhower had moved faster than had been thought possible; the Russians were allies who had lost seventeen million people in the struggle against the Nazis; it was considered desirable to induce the Russians to enter the war against Japan. Therefore, the Soviet Union should be given a fair share of Germany, even though this included territory the Red Army had not actually conquered and occupied.

Field soldiers like Colonel Toftoy, of course, were not asked for their opinions on this decision. They were, however, left to cope with its consequences. Another product of high-level diplomatic negotiation made those consequences border on the disastrous, in so far as evacuating V-2's to the United States was concerned. In November 1944, the European Advisory Commission, composed of American, British, and Russian delegates, had drafted a decree to be issued after the German surrender which stated in part that "all factories, plants, shops, research institutions, laboratories, testing stations, technical data, plans, drawings and inventions" must be held "intact and in good condition at the disposal of the Allied representatives, for such purposes and at such times and places as they may prescribe." [1]

This decree, in plain English, meant that the Americans were to leave to the Russians the *Mittelwerke,* with its V-2's and machine tools, in good condition. And this, of course, was exactly what the Russians wanted and needed to put them, almost overnight, into the long-range rocket business. Now, officially, Colonel Toftoy was suddenly not supposed to execute Trichel's order but to leave the V-2's to the Russians.

Faced with this dilemma, Colonel Toftoy was not one to give up easily. Now forty-one years old, he had graduated from West Point in 1926. He was six feet tall, lean, wore steel-rimmed glasses, and was considered the Army's leading expert, not on rockets, but on submarine mines. He had been sent to Europe to clear the harbors of northern France of mines after the Allied D-day landings, and in the course of this hazardous work had staged what was probably the biggest and noisiest Independence Day fireworks display ever held. This had taken place on July 4, 1944, at Cherbourg, when Toftoy had fired a network of hundreds of big underwater mines which the retreating Germans had dumped into the harbor in an effort to close it to Allied shipping. Before doing this, he had personally and at great risk defused the explosive in a previously unknown type of German submarine mine.

After he had also cleared the harbors of Granville, St. Malo, Brest, and Le Havre, he had become Chief of Ordnance Technical Intelligence, whose mission it was to locate and ship to the United States and the United Kingdom for further study interesting German operational weapons. He directed teams equipped with jeeps, radios, photographic equipment, and know-how and attached to all United States Army Groups, as well as a "gypsy team" which could be sent quickly into any area where something of interest turned up. These Ordnance Technical Intelligence teams had done an excellent job in Europe. The only difficulty Toftoy had encountered in accomplishing his missions came from the British.

United States Army Ordnance had a verbal understanding with its British counterpart, observed throughout World War II, that if two items of captured German equipment were found by the Americans, the latter would send one of them to the United Kingdom. If only one item was found, it would be sent, not to the Aberdeen Proving Ground in

Maryland, but to England, on the theory that since England was close to the continent a quicker study could be made there. In practice, Colonel Toftoy found that the British frequently resorted to this agreement to lay claim to captured German weapons, such as King Tiger tanks, which Toftoy's men had worked hard to procure and which he strongly felt should go to the United States.

While the war was still on, Toftoy could see some justification for sharing with the British what he uncovered. Now that the war was over he could see much less justification for it. And knowing how urgently Colonel Trichel wanted the V-2's for his new Army Ordnance Rocket Branch, he saw no reason at all to abandon them to another ally, the Soviet Union. Toftoy decided to instruct Special Mission V-2 to proceed, whatever the consequences might be.

A key role in evacuating the rockets was given to twenty-six-year-old Major James Hamill of New York City. A graduate of Fordham University in 1940 with a B.S. in physics, Hamill had entered the regular Army through the Fordham Reserve Officers Training Corps. He had served with Toftoy in the United States, and Toftoy had been impressed by his work and his gift for thinking quickly in tight, unusual situations.

Hamill, who had been in charge of an Ordnance Technical Intelligence section dealing with artillery, fire control, and submarine mines, recalls Toftoy telling him that officially nothing was supposed to be moved out of the future Russian Zone. "But unofficially," Toftoy said, "I'm telling you to see that those V-2's get to Antwerp. Remove all the material that you can, without making it too obvious that we've looted the place." Neither Hamill nor Toftoy could know at the time that they would later be assigned to supervising the reassembly and firing of these same V-2's in the New Mexico desert and that Hamill would be given one of the most unusual assignments in the history of the United States Army.

Major William Bromley, an Ordnance Officer who had graduated from Stanford in 1940 with Major Staver, was placed in charge of the technical operations of Special Mission V-2.[2] He was assisted by Dr. Louis Woodruff, an M.I.T. professor of electrical engineering who served as special adviser to Ordnance Technical Intelligence. The coordination of the entire mission was the responsibility of Major Hamill, who set up a base for this purpose in Fulda, sixty miles southwest of Nordhausen.

By the time of the formal German surrender at Reims on May 7, 1945, Bromley, Woodruff, and Hamill had reconnoitered the *Mittelwerke*. They found the problems connected with evacuating the V-2's before the Red Army entered Nordhausen to be staggering. The date for the American withdrawal had not been officially announced but was generally believed to be June 1.

The major problem was that completely assembled rockets were not conveniently available for shipment to Antwerp. Components and subassemblies would have to be selected in the tunnels of the *Mittelwerke*. The difficulty here was that Special Mission V-2 lacked an accurate parts list. The V-2 technical documents had not yet been discovered, and not one leading German rocket specialist, who could have been used as a guide to the selection of parts required for an engineering device of awesome complexity, had been found in the Nordhausen area.

Then it was determined that aerial bombardment had destroyed most of the key bridges and rail lines leading in and out of Nordhausen. A main railhead existed, but there were not enough trucks available to transport rocket components from the underground factory to this railhead. And while there was a vast reservoir of enlisted men in the area, few of them could be usefully employed in the tunnels. This work required not just enthusiasm and brute strength but a knowledge of machinery at least equivalent to that of a skilled garage mechanic. To fill the need for a unit of men with a basic knowledge of machinery, Major Bromley requested an immediate troop movement of the 144th Motor Vehicle Assembly Company from Cherbourg.

Cherbourg, however, was eight hundred miles from Nordhausen. As he waited for the 144th MVA to arrive, Major Bromley obtained the services of Company B, 47th Armored Infantry, 5th Armored Division, to throw a strict security cordon around the *Mittelwerke*. Until then it had been open to anyone who wanted to enter it, which had caused some unfortunate happenings. The former inmates of the Nordhausen and Dora concentration camps, in their fury at their German captors and frenzied joy at being freed from them, had destroyed many priceless rocket components and machine tools. German civilians from the ruined city of Nordhausen had scavenged the plant, stealing such items as the light bulbs which had illuminated it and wiring from costly rocket components whose loss made them useless. Investigators from the British armed forces had inspected the *Mittelwerke* at will. So, too, on a smaller scale, had Soviet Intelligence agents. Company B stopped all of this traffic. The battle-hardened tankers turned away from the *Mittelwerke* everyone who did not have a pass authorized by Special Mission V-2.

Dr. Woodruff was now able to proceed undisturbed. He had studied the intelligence reports on V-2 and had a good idea of what was needed to make up a complete rocket. The basic ingredients were available in the *Mittelwerke*. The small and intricate control systems which had guided V-2, however, had not been manufactured in the tunnels. After the move from Peenemünde, the men assigned to developing control systems had been assigned makeshift laboratory space in villages surrounding Nordhausen. As the Americans approached, these men had hidden the controls in nearby barns, schools, and beer halls. The Americans had to organize scouting parties which searched the countryside around Nordhausen for a radius of thirty miles before the control systems, without which the V-2 itself would be almost useless, were located and brought to the main railroad.

By May 18, the 144th MVA, under Captain E. W. Mandeville, had arrived from Cherbourg and was ready to go to work. The Red Army was still believed to be coming in on June 1. If Special Mission V-2 did not accomplish its objective by that date, the consequences were obvious to the men attached to the mission: the United States would get no V-2's at all.

One mile of one of the two main tunnels had to be cleared to enable flatcars and gondolas to move quickly in and then out with rocket parts. One hundred and fifty former slave laborers were hired to help with the hard physical labor of lifting and packing. The 144th MVA was attached to the 319th Ordnance Battalion, and the enlisted men of both units quickly learned how to recognize parts and sections of the unfamiliar V-2. The loading and packing operation should have been carried out around the clock. But one end of the tunnel had to be closed for security reasons, and the ventilating system had broken down when the plant was overrun by American combat troops. Thus the work in the tunnel had to be limited to eight hours a day. Gradually enough parts were brought out to make up a shipment of one hundred V-2's. The parts were trucked to the main railhead.

It was here that the greatest problem connected with the evacuation faced Major Hamill. It had been estimated that between 300 and 350 rail cars would be needed to move the components and subassemblies to the port of Antwerp. This would constitute the largest single shipment of captured enemy equipment in World War II. But the Army Transportation Corps had not yet been assigned to the unofficial project and in any case did not have at its disposal the loco- motives and trains that were needed. It appeared that the improvisation and backbreaking work that had gone into moving the parts for one hundred V-2's out of the tunnel to the main railhead would have one result: leaving them there for the disposal of the Russians.

It was here that the aerial bombardment of the key bridges leading in and out of Nordhausen, which had ap- peared as one of the major obstacles to completing Special Mission V-2, suddenly seemed like a blessing. The destruc- tion of the bridges had isolated in Nordhausen hundreds of German rail cars which normally would have been moved out of the area. Major Hamill considered that this German rolling stock, most of it in excellent condition, might be the solution to the transportation problem. Then he learned that the Army Transportation Corps had also noted this roll- ing stock. The corps intended to impound it and then move it over the one remaining railroad bridge to territory that would stay under American control. Major Hamill, of course, had no written orders which he could use to force Transpor- tation to permit him to use the German rail cars.

He passed the early evening hours of May 19, 1945, with his assistant, Technician Fifth Grade Bob Payne. Hamill complained bitterly to Payne that the next day the Transpor- tation Corps was scheduled to move the rolling stock needed for the V-2 evacuation out of Nordhausen over the one re- maining railroad bridge. Bob Payne was a quixotic type who had had his ups and downs in the Army, but Major Hamill considered him a good man to have around in a tight situa- tion. The two men parted company and went to bed, both complaining about the imminent departure of the rolling stock.

The rolling stock, however, did not depart. The next morning Transportation Corps officers discovered that the railroad bridge was unusable. It had been blown up with a dynamite charge sometime during the night. Military Intelligence investigators suspected that Werewolves—German guerrillas—had sabotaged it. The facts were never clearly established. In later years, Major Hamill would maintain that he had had nothing to do with dynamiting the bridge and that he had no proof that T/5 Bob Payne had done it, either, although Hamill would admit that Payne had been known to go out of channels to accomplish certain objectives in the past. In any case, the dynamiting of the bridge prevented the rolling stock from leaving Nordhausen and gave Major Hamill time to perform some liaison with Transportation and Engineer Corps officers in Nordhausen. He was able to convince them of the importance and urgency of Special Mission V-2. The Transportation Corps relinquished its claim to the rail cars, and the 1186th Combat Engineer Company repaired the railroad bridge and built another bridge connecting the *Mittelwerke* with the main railhead.

To run their railroad, Bromley and Hamill secured the services of former German railroad employees in the area. The Germans, happy to get any kind of work, cooperated to the full. On May 22, 1945, the first train was inspected by Bromley and Hamill and pronounced ready to roll with a cargo of crated, marked, and documented rocket components. Major Bromley, however, pointed out to Major Hamill that there had been neither the time nor the manpower available "to pack adequately all the bulky items of the V-2 and waterproof them for a standard ocean voyage." The first train, operated by German trainmen and guarded by combat men of the 5th Armored Division, sped south to Erfurt, where it was taken over by the U. S. Military Railway Service and routed to Belgium and the port of Antwerp.

Each day, for nine days thereafter, one train—averaging forty cars per train—left Nordhausen for Antwerp. The Russians were still expected in Nordhausen on June 1. The last train departed at 9:30 P.M. on May 31, "thus," Major Bromley reported to Colonel Toftoy, "completing the mission on this project." Three hundred and forty-one rail cars, with a total tonnage of approximately four hundred long tons, had been sent to the Antwerp docks.

The mission, however, had not really been completed. Major Hamill recalls that his lack of clear orders caused trouble as soon as the first trains arrived at the docks. One port officer, maintaining that he had no orders to handle the V-2 shipment, told Hamill to stop cluttering up the docks with "all that junk" and to "back that engine right out of my port or I'll do it for you."

Fortunately, Hamill had been issued a card by Supreme Headquarters, Allied Expeditionary Forces, to facilitate his work in Ordnance Technical Intelligence. The card, signed by Eisenhower, authorized Hamill to ship captured enemy equipment. Hamill used it to keep "the junk" on the docks. He then had to carry out further liaison with the other technical services to complete his mission. Liberty ships were made available. Belgian stevedores were hired to unload the 341 rail cars. The 144th MVA was returned from Nordhausen to recrate the rocket parts in frameworks for the ocean voyage to New Orleans, whence they would be moved by rail to the White Sands Proving Ground. At last, all of the warheads, tail assemblies, thrust units, special tools, fuel tanks and bodies, and control systems were ready to be hoisted into sixteen waiting Liberty ships.

Under the verbal agreement which U. S. Army Ordnance had fulfilled with the British throughout the war, however, the British were entitled to half of the V-2's. Colonel Toftoy, before he had organized Special Mission V-2, was aware of this, but in this particular case had decided not to allow the British a half share in the work done by his men. He made no effort to inform his British counterparts that the V-2's had been evacuated from Nordhausen and were ready for shipment, and he also recommended to his superiors that all of the rockets be sent to the United States.

But on the Antwerp docks British Intelligence agents noted the waiting Liberty ships and the crates of V-2 parts, grasped what was about to happen, and notified London. The British attempted to stop the shipment through strong protests registered by high-ranking officers attached to General Eisenhower's staff. Just before the protests could result in action, Colonel Joel Holmes, Chief of the Technical Division in Paris Ordnance Headquarters, made a decision. Colonel Holmes knew of the agreement for sharing captured enemy weapons with the British. He also knew that the British rocket people had followed V-2 more closely than either the Americans or the Russians had and admired the intelligence work the British had performed during the war. As Chief of the Technical Division, Holmes could postpone or cancel the Antwerp shipment.

"Maybe I was wrong," Holmes later said, "but I felt that more information could be obtained by sending them all back to the United States rather than half to England." He gave the order to ship. By the time the British officers attached to Eisenhower's staff had obtained the authorization to stop the shipment, the V-2's were on the high seas. "I had some explaining to do," Colonel Holmes later described the storm that descended upon him, "but nothing serious developed as far as I personally was concerned."

As a result of Holmes's order, the United States now had definite possession of one hundred V-2's. They would lose much of their value, however, if they were not accompanied by their technical documents. Parallel to Special Mission V-2, an operation had been going on to locate these documents and to ship them, too, in their entirety to the United States. But this operation had also been bedeviled by the lack of time and by the fact that, unlike the V-2 components in the *Mittelwerke,* the documents were still hidden. While the

V-2's were being shipped to Antwerp, and while the interrogations of Wernher von Braun, Walter Dornberger, and the other rocket specialists continued in Bavaria, the documents containing the entire story of V-2 remained in the small room at the end of the dynamited gallery in the abandoned mine at Dörnten.

# 13

## Treasure hunt

At dawn on Sunday, May 20, a two-seater Ford convertible roadster had left Nordhausen and headed toward the Harz Mountains. In the car were two German civilians. They were an unusual sight as they drove through mining villages and over deserted winding roads. Even the most casual observer must have wondered how two German civilians had procured a vehicle that would operate and enough gasoline to travel any distance. And the two men drove in a seemingly aimless fashion, pausing like tourists in village after village to ask local miners a single question. The question itself was unusual: Did the miners know the location of a certain abandoned mine?

The occupants of the car were Dr. Eberhard Rees and Karl Otto Fleischer. Since 1940, Dr. Rees had been the department chief in charge of the entire Peenemünde plant. Fleischer had served as business manager of the *Elektromechanische Werke* since its relocation from Peenemünde to Nordhausen. He was also the man to whom Huzel and Tessmann had confided the general location of the V-2 documents before they had gone to the Alps, and the only man in the Nordhausen-Bleicherode area who had any idea where they might be found.

Fleischer and Rees drove from dawn until well into the afternoon through the mining villages of the Harz with their question still unanswered. Then, at Andreasberg, they found an old miner who said he had once worked in a mine like the one Fleischer was describing. It was near Dörnten.

Fleischer and Rees left Andreasberg and after driving thirty miles at top speed emerged from the northern edge of the Harz. After driving another three miles, they came upon the abandoned mine, located its elderly superintendent and learned that their journey had ended: they had found the hiding place of the V-2 documents.

The man behind that journey was Major Robert Staver, and it had really begun three weeks before, when Staver had arrived in the ruined city of Nordhausen.

Reaching Nordhausen had constituted a problem in itself for Major Staver. By the end of April, some two weeks after its capture by the 3rd Armored Division, Nordhausen was still classified as a combat area. Because of the ban against technical investigators entering combat zones, Staver had been unable to get clearance.

He finally went to Colonel Toftoy with his problem. Although Staver was not assigned to Ordnance Technical Intelligence,* Toftoy felt that the mission Staver had been

---

* In the spring of 1945, the organization to which both Colonel Toftoy and Major Staver were attached was officially known as Office, Chief of Ordnance, European Theater of Operations. The Chief Ordnance Officer was Major General Henry B. Sayler. Under General Sayler was a Technical Division, headed by Colonel Joel G. Holmes. The Technical Division was in turn divided into two independent branches, Ordnance Technical Intelligence under Colonel Toftoy, which was concerned with enemy weapons that were operational and in actual use in combat, and Research and Development, under Colonel Horace B. Quinn, which was concerned with enemy weapons that might have future research and development applications. Major Staver's Rocket Section was under Colonel Quinn. There was a certain parallel work carried out by both branches of the Technical Division concerning the V-2, which was both

given by Colonel Trichel was important. Toftoy realized that the only way to get Staver into Nordhausen was to assign him to an outfit that was already there. Toftoy had such an outfit, Ordnance Technical Intelligence Team No. 1, which was attached to the First Army in Nordhausen at the very moment that Staver came to see him.

Colonel Toftoy, a West Pointer and a career soldier, was also a man who could be flexible where important objectives were concerned. When faced with a new type of German controlled submarine mine which had to be defused and examined in order to effect the clearing of Cherbourg Harbor quickly, he had simply sent everybody out of the possible reach of the mine's high explosive and taken it apart himself. Now he issued fake orders to Staver, stating that Major Robert Staver was assigned to Ordnance Technical Intelligence Team No. 1 and could proceed from Paris Ordnance Headquarters to Nordhausen.

The ruse worked. Major Staver and Ed Hull, a General Electric engineer from the Hermes Project, arrived in Nordhausen on April 30, 1945. They proceeded to investigate the *Mittelwerke* and scores of other plants and laboratories scattered throughout the Harz Mountains. But by May 12, Major Staver had still not located any of the *Elektromechanische Werke* personnel. These German rocket specialists, of course, had no way of knowing Wernher von Braun had voluntarily surrendered to the Americans in the Alps on May 2, because there was no radio, telephone, or any other means of communication for civilians between Nordhausen and Garmisch. The EW personnel in Nordhausen had simply faded away

---

operational and had future research and development potential. Colonel Toftoy gave Major Staver a great deal of encouragement and support, even though Staver was not officially assigned to Toftoy's Ordnance Technical Intelligence teams.

into scores of surrounding villages; unlike von Braun, none of them took the initiative of going directly to the Americans. But on the evening of May 12, Major Staver followed up an intelligence tip and located Karl Otto Fleischer in Nordhausen. Now that the war was over, Fleischer decided to cooperate with the Americans. However, he kept to himself the fact that he was the only man in Nordhausen who had any knowledge of the hiding place of the V-2 documents. Instead, he led Major Staver to Dr. Eberhard Rees, who in turn cooperated and introduced Staver to many of the other key figures in the German rocket program who had remained in the Nordhausen area.

On May 14, in a jail at Saalfeld, sixty miles from Nordhausen, Major Staver located a man who, like Dr. Rees, had been one of the leading figures at Peenemünde. This was Walther Riedel, who had been chief of the rocket motor and structural design section. In a case of mistaken identity, Riedel had been arrested by U. S. Counter-Intelligence agents, who thought he had worked on poison-gas development and a "bacteria bomb." According to Staver, Riedel had lost several front teeth in the course of being questioned by Counter-Intelligence. With the intervention of U. S. Military Government officers, Major Staver obtained Riedel's release from the Saalfeld jail and brought him to Nordhausen for interrogation on May 16, 17, and 18.

Riedel cooperated fully with Major Staver, who obtained from him a complete picture of rocket research in Germany. But like von Braun, who was being interrogated at the same time by Dr. Porter in Garmisch, Riedel treated the military application of the V-2 as a sidelight. According to Riedel, what the Peenemünde group was really interested in (and Staver reported this to Paris Ordnance Headquarters for transmittal to the Pentagon in May 1945) were "passenger-carrying rockets, trips to space stations revolving about the earth as satellites, space mirrors which could be used for good and possibly evil, short trips around the moon, and daring explorations of outer space."

Walther Riedel also suggested to Major Staver that it would be a wise move on the part of the Americans to import at least a part of the vast Peenemünde organization, perhaps forty of the key men, to the United States to continue their work. If the Americans did not take this step, the Russians might do so. Riedel had heard a rumor that the Russians were coming into Nordhausen to replace the American Army on June 1. Staver knew that this was no longer a rumor and that the Russians definitely were moving into Nordhausen. He sent a letter by courier to Paris Ordnance Headquarters recommending that a hundred of the key Peenemünde personnel in American custody be evacuated to the United States within thirty days to be employed by the Ordnance Department. In Staver's view, they could be used for the immediate purpose of completing development of the revolutionary *Wasserfall* anti-aircraft rocket, which could be used in the Pacific war if it were unduly prolonged. Staver felt that this argument would carry weight with Ordnance officers in the Pentagon. Actually, he hoped that once the Germans were brought to the United States they could continue, after the Japanese war was over, their research on long-range guided missiles.

While interrogating Riedel, Rees, and other leading rocket men in Nordhausen, however, Staver had been unable to learn from them one vital fact: the location of the V-2 documents. He had assisted in the location of various rocket components for the Special Mission V-2 evacuation project, but he knew that the hundred V-2's would be almost impossible to reassemble and test-fire at the White Sands Proving Ground without their accompanying drawings and blueprints. None of the rocket specialists he questioned, however, seemed to know or to be willing to admit where the documents were.

On the afternoon of May 18, a plane arrived from Brunswick with Drs. Frankel and Robertson, two civilian technical investigators attached to General Eisenhower's headquarters. They had come to pick up Riedel, Rees, and any other key Peenemünde personnel Major Staver had located in Nordhausen and fly them to Garmisch. Staver refused to relinquish his charges, and presented a strong case against doing this. He pointed out that it would disrupt his own interrogations which were going so well, and that the men in question were doing an important job in tracking down equipment which was not available in Bavaria. Possibly they also might be induced to reveal the location of the V-2 documents, and there was not much time left to accomplish this objective with the Russians supposedly moving in on June 1.

Dr. Robertson agreed with Staver's view, then glanced through his pocket notebook and read a notation: "Von Ploetz said that General Dornberger told General Rossman that documents of V-weapon production were hidden in *Kaliwerke* (salt mine) at Bleicherode, walled into one of the mine shafts. Von Ploetz was G-2 to Kammler." Dr. Robertson suggested that Rees or Fleischer might be able to direct Major Staver to the salt mine in question, but other than that Dr. Robertson had no further information to offer.

Major Staver spent the rest of the afternoon interrogating Walther Riedel with the thought constantly in the back of his mind of how to turn Dr. Robertson's sketchy lead to the best advantage. The V-2 documents, of course, were not in the salt mine at Bleicherode, which contained only some minor material relating to production. At 6 P.M., Staver left the U. S. Military Government building with Riedel and found that Fleischer had been waiting for them in his two-seater roadster. As casually as he could, after a few words of greeting with Fleischer, Staver took out his own pocket notebook and read from it: "Von Braun, Steinhoff, and all the others who fled to the south have been interned at Garmisch. Our intelligence officers have talked to von Ploetz, General Dornberger, General Rossman, and General Kammler. They told us that many of your drawings and important documents were buried underground in a mine somewhere around here, and that Riedel, or *you*, Fleischer, could help us find them."

This was, of course, a fabrication designed to make Fleischer and Riedel think they had been put on the spot by their superiors. Staver reasoned that if they did have any knowledge of a cache of documents they would believe either that they had to tell him where it was or risk being imprisoned for withholding information their superiors wanted the Americans to have. Major Staver's gamble appeared to produce no reaction whatever from Riedel. Staver, however, recalls that a puzzled expression came over Karl Otto Fleischer's face and that his brow wrinkled and his jaw dropped. He said nothing, however. Staver, not wanting to appear as eager as he was to find the documents, told the two Germans to think over very carefully what he had said and to meet him at eleven o'clock the next morning in Bleicherode.

Again not wanting to seem overly anxious, Staver arrived purposely late in Bleicherode at noon the next day. Riedel was there, but Fleischer was not. This disturbed Staver, until Riedel told him that Fleischer was waiting in the nearby village of Haynrode and had "some very important news" to tell Staver.

Staver and Riedel drove to Haynrode and pulled up before The Inn of the Three Lime Trees. Riedel, who was a big blond extrovert and, like most of the Peenemünde engineers, still a young man under thirty-five, barged into the inn and asked the proprietress for a message that was to have been left for him by Herr Fleischer. The message was produced. Riedel read it and beckoned Major Staver to follow him. They walked up a narrow alley to the edge of the village and the home of the local priest. The priest, who spoke excellent English, said that Herr Fleischer was upstairs and that he would send for him.

Fleischer came down, looking haggard and as though he

had not slept at all the previous night. He politely asked the priest to leave and led Staver under some blossoming apple trees. Staver recalls that in almost inaudible, somewhat apologetic tones Fleischer admitted he had not been completely frank with him. He did have a general idea where the Peenemünde documents were hidden and believed he was the only one in Nordhausen who did. Von Braun, Tessmann, and Huzel knew where they were hidden, too, but of course those men were four hundred miles away in Garmisch. Fleischer had not wanted to take it upon himself to divulge the hiding place to the Americans, but if his superiors wanted him to do so he no longer saw any need for withholding the information. Major Staver insisted that this was indeed the case.

Fleischer now spoke in louder, firmer tones. The documents were not walled up in a salt mine in Bleicherode; this mine contained only minor production papers. The principal cache was at least thirty miles away in an abandoned mine of which Fleischer had been given a description. The mine was supposed to be near the village of Doren (it was, of course, in Dörnten; there was no village of Doren, and the slight confusion in spelling would later cause Fleischer to drive around the mountains for nearly an entire day before finding the true location of the mine). Fleischer asked Major Staver for permission to conduct a search the next day with Dr. Eberhard Rees. But Fleischer suggested that the search would have a greater chance of success if an American officer was not in the search party.

Staver had to think quickly about that proposition. He decided to risk trusting Fleischer and Rees. He provided them with gasoline and passes to drive into the neighboring counties and to travel after the 8 P.M. curfew for German civilians. The next day, May 20, Major Staver, wondering if he would ever see Fleischer and Rees again, jeeped with Walther Riedel to Lehesten to conduct an investigation of

two test stands where rocket motors had been tested. At
1:30 P.M. the following day, Staver returned to Bleicherode in
a driving rainstorm. He went immediately to Fleischer's house
and found him sprawled on a davenport. He and Rees,
Fleischer said wearily, had found the documents.

It had not, however been an easy mission to bring to a successful conclusion. When Fleischer and Rees had arrived at
the mine and located Herr Nebelung, its elderly caretaker,
Nebelung had stoutly maintained that there was no material
of any kind hidden in the mine. It was only after an hour of
argument, with Fleischer insisting that he was a director of
the German rocket program and was acting under the orders
of the generals who had been in charge of the program, that
Nebelung relented and admitted that three trucks had come
to the mine in early April with tons of boxes, which had been
hidden in a small room at the end of a gallery. Getting them
out of the room, however, was another matter; the gallery
leading to it had been sealed off with dynamite charges, and
only the day before Nebelung had blasted another ten cubic
yards of rock into the gallery entrance.

Fleischer had persuaded Nebelung to begin excavation
work immediately, assuring him that he would be well paid
for his cooperation. Miners from the area who were otherwise unemployed were rounded up and put to work in three
shifts around the clock, although only two men could be assigned to each shift because of the narrow width of the gallery. Before returning to Bleicherode with Dr. Rees, Fleischer
had told Nebelung that American officers would shortly go to
Dörnten to direct the final phases of the excavation and to
collect the boxes.

There was now no doubt in Major Staver's mind that the
search for the most important documents in Germany was
over. Serious problems in taking full advantage of the find,
however, remained. It was now May 21. Staver had learned
that in another shift of zonal boundaries similar to the one

that would bring the Russians into Nordhausen, the British were due to replace the Americans in the Dörnten area on May 27. That gave Major Staver just six days to carry out an evacuation for which considerable trucking facilities would be needed. If he failed, all the V-2 documents would go to the British.

Major Staver left Fleischer and Rees, tracked down Lieutenant Hochmuth of Ordnance Technical Intelligence Team No. 1., and instructed him to go to Dörnten the next morning with Fleischer to supervise the excavation. Because no radio or telephone communication existed between Nordhausen and Paris, Staver decided he would have to fly to Paris Ordnance Headquarters to obtain the authorization for the manpower and the ten-ton trucks that would be needed to transport the boxes into territory that would remain under American control. At 3 A.M. on the morning of May 22, Staver awakened Major William Bromley, his old Stanford classmate, who assigned him a jeep and a driver to speed to the nearest air base in Kassel, forty miles away.

Arriving in Kassel at dawn, Staver discovered that no cargo or passenger planes were scheduled to fly to Orly Field, Paris, that day. There was, however, a P-47 Thunderbolt fighter about to take off for Paris. Staver, who had no written orders authorizing air travel to Paris, pleaded with the pilot of the P-47 to permit him to hitchhike along. The pilot had no objection to helping a fellow officer reach Paris, but he pointed out that the Thunderbolt was a single-seat fighter. Staver went to the plane and saw some space behind its one seat. He told the pilot it was so urgent that he reach Paris quickly that he would be willing to ride piggy-back for the two-hour flight. The pilot considered this unusual request for a few moments, then told Staver that since the war was over he could see no reason why anyone would object to his granting it.

The Thunderbolt, with Staver half sitting, half standing

behind the pilot, sometimes straddling his shoulders, left Kassel and streaked toward Paris at tree-top level because of a low cloud ceiling. It arrived at Orly Field around 10 A.M., and from there Staver hitchhiked in an army jeep to the Champs-Élysées and Ordnance Headquarters. He went to Colonel Joel Holmes, Chief of the Technical Division, who had once been Staver's R.O.T.C. instructor at Stanford, and told him that the documents had been found. Arrangements were made to have two ten-ton semi-trailers meet Staver in Nordhausen. This was not Staver's only objective in flying to Paris, however. Following up the report he had already sent from Nordhausen, he made a strong presentation to Colonel Holmes about the wisdom of sending at least a part of the Peenemünde organization to the United States. To make this proposal more attractive from the immediate military angle, he played up the help that the *Wasserfall* anti-aircraft rocket might subsequently be in the war against Japan.

"All right, Bob," Staver recalls Colonel Holmes telling him. "It's unusual, but it makes sense to me. You write the cable and I'll sign it."

That same day, May 22, 1945, a cable bearing a "Secret" classification was sent from Ordnance, Technical Division, in Paris to the Pentagon for the attention of Colonel Trichel:

> Have in custody over 400 top research development personnel of Peenemünde. Developed V-2. Latest development named Wasserfall, a 3000 kg flak rocket. . . . Believe this development would be important for Pacific war. The research directors believe if their group were taken to U.S. that after one month of adjustment and reorganization and three months of hard work could reproduce complete drawings of Wasserfall. The research directors and staff realize impossibility for continuation of rocket development in Germany. Most are under 35 and know no other type of work. They are anxious to carry on their research in whatever country will give them the opportunity, preferably U.S., second England, third France.

. . . The thinking of the scientific directors of this group is 25 years ahead of U.S. . . . Have begun development of A-10 to have thrust about 220,000 pounds. Later version of this rocket should permit launching from Europe to U.S.

Recommend that 100 of very best men of this research organization be evacuated to U.S. immediately for purpose of reconstructing complete drawings of Wasserfall. Also recommend evacuation of all material drawings and documents belonging to this group to aid their work in the U.S.

Immediate action recommended to prevent loss of whole or part of this group to other interested agencies. . . . Urgently request reply as early as possible.[1]

With the cable sent, Major Staver flew back to Germany the next morning, May 23, and got in touch with the 9th Army Ordnance officer, Colonel Warner, at Brunswick. Colonel Warner drove to the Dörnten mine with Staver and placed a twenty-four-hour guard from the 83rd Division around it. Staver inspected the mine and saw that the gallery had not yet been cleared, with the British definitely taking over the area in four days. Staver learned from Lieutenant Hochmuth why he and Fleischer had been delayed in completing the excavation work, and the explanation heightened Staver's sense of urgency about completing the operation quickly.

Two days before, a party of British officers and enlisted men had appeared, ostensibly searching for hidden German firearms. Lieutenant Hochmuth, who was in work clothes and spoke some German, and Fleischer pretended they were geologists as they conversed with each other in German. Word was passed to the German miners to cover up where they had been digging and to start looking for ore samples. While the British party looked on, samples of low-grade iron ore were actually boxed for transport. Digging for the documents had to be suspended for the entire day until the British satisfied themselves that there were no firearms hidden in the area and departed.

Major Staver now directed that the work of clearing the gallery be speeded up. By Saturday, May 26, with the British due to take over Dörnten the next day at 10 A.M., the gallery had been cleared and the boxes taken out of the mine on flatcars. They were piled up in front of the tunnel entrance, waiting to be loaded onto trucks and driven away, when Staver discovered that the ten-ton trucks for which he had obtained authorization in Paris had not yet arrived in Nordhausen. Staver quickly telephoned Lieutenant Colonel Wood, Colonel Warner's executive officer, who authorized the 71st Ordnance Battalion in Nordhausen to furnish six two-and-a-half-ton trucks for Staver's use.

At 6 A.M. on the morning of the British take-over, Staver and Major Bromley led the convoy of six trucks through the Harz Mountains to Dörnten. They arrived at the mine, supervised the quick loading of the boxes into the trucks, and headed back to American-occupied territory, reaching it just as the British began to set up their roadblocks.

The fourteen tons of recovered documents were stored in Nordhausen for five days until the two ten-ton trucks finally arrived. Then, escorted by armed guards in two jeeps, the documents were transferred to Paris and then shipped to the Foreign Documents Evaluation Center at the Aberdeen Proving Ground, Maryland. Again, the British, who had followed the V-2 more closely than either the Americans or the Russians since the beginning of the secret weapon investigation, had lost out in the postwar competition for the V-2 secrets. The Americans now had full possession of one hundred V-2's and all the key V-2 documents. There was, however, still one side to the V-2 triangle which the Americans did not yet have in their complete possession: the German rocket men themselves. While all of these men and their families were in areas under American control, the Americans had not yet effected a plan to get them out of Germany and to the United States. And while the Peenemünde men remained in Germany itself, British Intelligence would continue a concerted effort to take them away from the Americans and to enlist their services in the United Kingdom.

Soviet Intelligence, too, had marked the German rocket men as a priority target. The Soviet effort, beginning in May 1945, would prove more successful than the British and would have an end result that would startle the world.

# 14

## Exodus

An advance party of Soviet officers had arrived in Nordhausen on May 26, 1945, the day before Major Staver had evacuated the V-2 documents from Dörnten and five days before the last trainload of V-2 components was dispatched to Antwerp by Majors Bromley and Hamill. The Russians had come to inspect the *Mittelwerke*.

There was no way that the Americans could refuse to issue passes authorizing the Russian party to pass through the security cordon of the 5th Armored Division and inspect the tunnels of the V-2 factory. The Soviets were allies; they had permitted the British-American Crossbow Committee team to inspect the Blizna firing range in Poland which had been taken by the Red Army in September 1944; they were, in any case, soon to take over the area in which the *Mittelwerke* was located.

The news of the early arrival of the inspection party underscored for Major Staver his long-standing conviction that the Soviets were strongly interested in V-2 and that this interest included German rocket personnel. He had learned that the Russians were radio-broadcasting frequent appeals to anyone formerly associated with Peenemünde to go to Dresden to see a Dr. de Pinsky, who was organizing a German group to continue rocket research in Germany itself. The working conditions and pay offered sounded highly attractive in a country where unemployment, hunger, and mere survival were now major problems. When Staver had driven up to the Elbe in search of hidden rocket equipment, he had been startled to hear loudspeakers on the Red Army side of the river blaring requests for German rocket men to come over from the American side to accept well-paying offers. A bonus of fifty thousand reichsmarks was offered to Wernher von Braun and Ernst Steinhoff.

Von Braun, Steinhoff, Dornberger, and many of the other important Germans were, of course, still in American custody in Garmisch. The difficulty was that they had been sent to the Alps by Kammler without their families, who remained in the area of central Germany soon to be transferred to Soviet control. In addition, many of the key German rocket men, such as Walther Riedel and Eberhard Rees, had not gone to the Alps. Unless the American authorities took quick action, Major Staver realized that the Russians would, by default, capture such men as Riedel, Rees, and Karl Otto Fleischer, some four thousand technicians and their families who had stayed in the Nordhausen area, and the families of the five hundred rocket men who had gone to Bavaria. Staver knew that it would be almost impossible to induce the men who were in Garmisch to accept employment in the United States if their families were held by the Soviet Secret Police. But Staver did not possess the authority to order a mass exodus of Germans from the future Soviet Zone.

On the night of May 27, however, after Staver had effected the evacuation of the V-2 documents from Dörnten, he was given the transcript of a telephone message from Paris which had been sent two days before to Fulda, eighty miles southwest of Nordhausen. The message relayed to Major Staver by Colonel Holger Toftoy stated that "Paris and Washington are both working on the problem of evacuating the

German technicians and their families. In the meantime it is requested that you remove the German technicians and their families to an area under U.S. control."

Major Staver interpreted this message as preliminary approval for the cable he had prepared recommending the evacuation of a hundred Peenemünde specialists to the United States, which had been signed by Colonel Holmes and sent to Ordnance in the Pentagon on May 22. Indeed, though officers in the field in Germany could not know it, high-level discussions concerning the future disposition of German scientists were going on in the War Department. These secret discussions eventually led to a unique project bearing the code designation *Overcast,* which involved not just rocket men but thousands of German scientists who were of interest to all branches of the American armed forces. But as of May 27, 1945, final approval had not been given to bring Germans to the United States under *Overcast.* The War Department did, however, want certain German scientists evacuated from the future Soviet Zone while the complex details of *Overcast* were being worked out.

To the policy makers in Washington the evacuation decision might have seemed a logical and simple step. But to Major Staver the implementation of the decision presented formidable problems. Although several of the engineers he had interrogated had expressed interest in continuing their work in the United States, Staver had no assurances that the majority would agree to moving themselves and their families to a new area at a moment's notice without a firm commitment from the Americans of future employment. To locate and then evacuate some four thousand people and their belongings from the future Soviet Zone by June 1, or in less than a week, would be well nigh impossible. Staver knew that he would be lucky to get a few score of the key people out within that time limit. However, he immediately set his small organization to work to accomplish what he could.

In the atmosphere of May 1945, when the cold war had not yet started and Germans were regarded as Nazi enemies, not all American officers with whom Staver had to work looked upon the evacuation project as important or even desirable. In fact, one high-ranking Ordnance officer, who was in a position to offer administrative help to Staver, told him bluntly: "I don't care if the Russians get all of those Krauts. I say good riddance." Another officer upon whom Staver had tried to impress the fact that the long-range thinking of the Peenemünde group could lead to intercontinental ballistic missiles and space exploration told him to "forget that Buck Rogers stuff."

The evacuation was undertaken, nevertheless, and the project received a vital break when the Red Army did not move into Thuringia on June 1 as it had been generally expected to do. The breathing spell, however, was to be a short one; the Russians were officially scheduled to come in on June 21. "The fateful decision," as Winston Churchill described the manner in which a defeated Germany would be divided among the Allies, had been made at the Yalta Conference in February 1945. The occupation zones had been agreed upon by Churchill, Roosevelt, and Stalin, but when the Third Reich surrendered, the positions of the Allied armies did not coincide with those zones. The Americans had swept to the Elbe River and occupied vast sections of Saxony and Thuringia which had been allocated to the Russians. Churchill felt strongly that the Americans should display no undue haste in withdrawing from the heart of Germany, but should delay their departure at least until the Potsdam Conference in July, when some troublesome problems that had arisen with the Soviet Union could be settled.

President Truman, who had had nothing to do with the fixing of the zones at Yalta, declined to go along with Churchill's view. His advisers had counseled him that relations with Stalin would be harmed by postponing action until Potsdam. Truman therefore sent a message to Stalin that all American troops would begin withdrawing to their assigned occupation zone on June 21.

"This," Churchill later wrote, "struck a knell in my breast." [1] On the level of Major Staver and the other Ordnance officers who had been assigned the evacuation project, the decision had exactly the same effect, though the language they employed to describe their feelings was not Churchillian.

One of the first steps that Staver took to organize the evacuation was to request that von Braun and the Peenemünde department chiefs be flown from Garmisch to Nordhausen. On June 8, Ernst Steinhoff and Martin Schilling arrived. Staver asked them, as well as Rees and Riedel, to tell him, without comparing estimates, the number of people who would be essential for future research and to supply their names. The figures ranged from a low of 350 to a high of 750.

With these figures and names in hand, Staver then assigned the four Germans to help his junior officers track down and evacuate the most important of the four thousand people scattered around Thuringia. At this time no contracts could be offered to the German rocket specialists for work in the United States. The only firm offer that Major Staver and his men were authorized to make to the Germans was the opportunity to leave the area which would shortly become the Russian Zone for a place in the American Zone where they would be housed and fed.

Lieutenant George Gross, of Staver's command, who worked closely with Dr. Ernst Steinhoff in locating the rocket personnel and directing them to a central staging area, later observed: "One thing which irritated me the most was a question which constantly would arise from the German scientists and engineers. 'What kind of treatment can we expect from the United States for our assistance as compared to the approaches made by the Russians?' . . . The Russians, the

German engineers said, were baiting them with homes, research facilities and special consideration for continuing their missile developments. We did not have any such bait and it became extremely confusing to deal with this high caliber of personnel and sell them a bill of goods void of all promises, and threats didn't seem to be the right thing. The biggest help was through the German scientists themselves feeling closer to the Americans. . . ."

Wernher von Braun, who by this time had begun to think that the Americans might do something about his idea of continuing the work of Peenemünde in the United States, proved to be a major factor in locating the rocket men in Thuringia and persuading them to go to the American Zone.

On June 19, two days before the official date of the Soviet take-over, Staver and Lt. Col. R. L. Williams, an officer recently assigned to rocket investigations by Paris Ordnance Headquarters, went to Garmisch and took Dr. Richard Porter, von Braun and the latter's remaining department chiefs by jeep to Munich. From here they were all flown to Nordhausen.

This quick movement from Bavaria was prompted by the need of locating all of the important Peenemünde engineers and their families and moving them to American territory before the Soviets entered Thuringia. For by now, Colonel Trichel had requested that Dr. Porter participate in the selection of V-2 personnel to be brought to the United States. These selections were to be started in Nordhausen by Staver and Dr. Porter in consultation with von Braun and his department chiefs. They could not, of course, be completed until after the key men and their families were evacuated to the west.

Once in Nordhausen, where, two weeks before, Staver had initiated the selection of V-2 personnel, Dr. Porter discovered that a transportation problem existed. Although he was a civilian, Dr. Porter found himself joining Ordnance officers in pleading and begging for anything that would roll—jeeps, half-tracks, trucks. Some three hundred vehicles were assembled and sent out, as Porter noted, "each with a German on board who personally knew the people to be contacted, in order to explain the situation and ask the people to come. This went on for twenty-four hours, but each family had only about fifteen minutes to decide and pack up what they could carry. Most of them came eagerly."

The rocket men and their families were gradually rounded up and gathered in a central staging area near the Nordhausen railroad station. The last of the Germans were brought in at noon on July 20, twenty-four hours before the Red Army was scheduled to arrive. Lieutenant Gross noticed boxcars and passenger cars waiting on a siding but could see no sign of an engine. "The Germans were apprehensive," Gross later said, "and I was close to being a mental case waiting at the station. Every time a German would say Russky I would jump ten feet."

Gross was about to abandon rail transportation and redirect the Germans into an improvised car and truck convoy, when the engine finally arrived. Over a thousand Germans hurriedly boarded fifty rail cars, and the train sped out of Nordhausen, eventually reaching Witzenhausen, a small town in the American Zone, forty miles to the southwest.

There were no armed guards at the Nordhausen railroad station or on the train because none were needed. The V-2 personnel were only too happy to get away from the incoming Russians. In fact, the only problem connected with the final stage of the evacuation was the appearance at the Nordhausen station of throngs of displaced persons, and German civilians who had not been attached to the rocket program, who attempted to fight their way into the rail cars before they left for the American Zone. These people did have to be prevented from boarding the already overcrowded train by armed American soldiers.

The departure of the train, however, did not end the problems of Dr. Porter and Major Staver. Not all of the Peenemünde documents had been recovered in the Dörnten operation. Before going to the Alps, General Dornberger had hidden his own papers somewhere near Bad Sachsa. They represented a prize that could not be left for the Russians to find.

Dr. Porter organized a search party, but with only twelve hours left before the Red Army was scheduled to arrive, Dornberger's documents had still not been found, principally because the searchers lacked a large-scale German country map. In desperation, Dr. Porter and Major Staver drove sixty miles from Nordhausen to the headquarters of the 332nd Engineer Regiment in Kassel. They hoped that the Engineers would have a suitable map, but they did not. On a final gamble, Porter and Staver persuaded the regiment's executive officer to send out a small search team.

Sergeant Joseph Schwartz of Cleveland, Ohio, and three enlisted men left Kassel in a small truck. They brought with them shovels, a pick, and a mine detector. Sergeant Schwartz turned up a large-scale map in a German Forest Bureau and used it to find the general location of Dornberger's papers, which were in five boxes. Then, using the mine detector, Schwartz located the boxes themselves; they were made of wood, but their metal lining was enough to make the mine detector effective. The sergeant and his men dug up the five boxes, which had a total weight of 250 pounds, loaded them into their truck, and drove back to Kassel in the American Zone.

Thus, as of June 21, 1945, the Americans appeared to have won almost all of the V-2 spoils of war and an unbeatable lead over their Soviet and British allies in using them to build a postwar long-range rocket program. The United

States Army had all of the originals of the key Peenemünde documents, one hundred V-2's, and all of the leading German rocket figures. Nevertheless, Soviet Intelligence had not lost completely the race for the V-2 secrets.

As a result of the American withdrawal, the Russians would fall heir to the *Mittelwerke,* the rocket-motor test station at Lehesten, and the extensive research facilities at Bleicherode, Sondershausen, and Klein-Bodungen. And while the Americans had evacuated the leading German rocket experts from Nordhausen, there had been neither time nor manpower available to evacuate all of the Peenemünde personnel. Some three thousand rocket men and their families had been left behind. These men, while not capable of future creative rocket development, did have the expertise to operate the existing physical facilities.

On April 26, 1945, Joint Chiefs of Staff Order 1067 had been issued to General Eisenhower, directing him to "preserve from destruction and take under your control records, plans, books, documents, papers, files and scientific, industrial and other information and data belonging to . . . German organizations engaged in military research." [2] And on June 5, 1945, in Berlin, Eisenhower had signed the European Advisory Commission decree which, among other things, stipulated that German military research installations would be "held intact and in good condition at the disposal of Allied representatives for such purposes as they may prescribe."

Before leaving Nordhausen, Dr. Porter took a long last look at the rocket facilities which the Americans, honoring JCOS Order 1067 and the European Advisory Commission decree, left intact for the incoming Russians. Seventeen years later he would say: "I wanted to blow up the whole factory at Nordhausen before we pulled out, but . . . I couldn't swing it legally. I was afraid at the time to do the job 'unofficially,' and have regretted it ever since."

# 15

## Overcast

The Red Army units that moved into Nordhausen on the heels of the departing Americans* were accompanied by technical specialists from Malenkov's Special Committee, who were pleasantly astounded by what they found at the *Mittelwerke* and the rocket facilities surrounding it.

Unlike Peenemünde, which had been wrecked by British and American air raids and German demolition, the *Mittelwerke*—lying two hundred feet underground—had not been damaged. The underground factory was in almost as good operating condition as it had been when SS General Kammler's slave laborers were producing six hundred V-2's a month in its maze of tunnels. The Americans had evacuated parts for one hundred V-2's, and the British and French

* The American Army did not withdraw on the scheduled date of June 21, 1945, but on July 1. The withdrawal was to coincide with the entry of Anglo-American troops into Russian-occupied Berlin, and Stalin was in no hurry for this to take place. Stalin advised Churchill and Truman that Marshal Zhukov and other Soviet field commanders would have to be present in Moscow for a meeting of the Supreme Soviet and a great parade scheduled for June 24. As the commanders could not return to Germany before June 28 at the earliest, July 1 was suggested as a preferable date both for the British and American armies to enter Berlin and to withdraw from East Germany.

had taken the parts for a few more, but the Russians discovered components and subassemblies that could be used for the construction of hundreds of rockets. The Soviet technical team also found thousands of machine tools for rocket production, and although it did not find the original V-2 documents, it did find some copies, including blueprints for the projected A-9/A-10 intercontinental missile.

It will be recalled that Konstantin Tsiolkovsky, a Russian school teacher, had first published theories about rockets and space travel in 1903 and was regarded as one of the three great pioneers of modern rocketry, along with the American, Robert Goddard, and the German, Hermann Oberth. The Red Army had conducted experiments with rockets throughout the twenties and thirties. But in spite of these experiments and Tsiolkovsky's pioneering, the Soviet Union, at the close of World War II, had actually developed nothing more advanced than small powder rockets mounted on Sturmovik aircraft and Katyusha (Little Kitty), batteries of rockets mounted on Studebaker trucks and fired into German infantry with dreadful, panic-creating effect.[1] At Nordhausen, the Russians came into sudden possession of the world's first and only long-range rocket and thousands of men who know how to design and manufacture it.

British and American Intelligence agents observed what the Soviets were doing with their windfall and ascertained that none of the bulky equipment was being shipped to Russia. However, Intelligence also noted that the Soviet Secret Police was rounding up former *Elektromechanische Werke* employees who had not been evacuated to the American Zone and inducing them to return to work. In the great majority of cases, force was not needed. A technician in the Germany of 1945 could watch his family starve or try to keep afloat by repairing radios, bicycles, and automobile transmissions or return to the work he knew best. The Russians offered jobs at good wages, with many special privileges, and there was no indication that anyone would be forced to leave East Germany to work in the Soviet Union.

In early July 1945, American Intelligence could discern no clear pattern of Soviet intentions in regard to the closely guarded *Mittelwerke*. Intelligence did know, however, that the Russians lacked one vital element for the full exploitation of their Nordhausen windfall. In their zone, the Soviets controlled thousands of engineers, foremen, and production men. But at Witzenhausen and Eschwege, the Americans held the guiding figures of the German rocket program, the only men who had the creative ability to carry out large-scale future development.

There were vulnerable spots in the favored American position, however. Soviet agents were making attractive offers to anyone who had worked at Peenemünde. Until von Braun, Dornberger, Kurt Debus, Helmut Gröttrup, Eberhard Rees, Ernst Steinhoff, and the other key rocket men were evacuated to the United States, Soviet Intelligence had the opportunity to lure some of them back to Nordhausen. It was obvious that the rocket experts in the American Zone, some sixty miles away, would not remain there indefinitely without any firm assurance concerning their future. It became imperative as the weeks passed that the plan to bring them to the United States, which was being worked on in the Pentagon, be put into action.

On June 24, 1945, Colonel Holger Toftoy was in Brussels, en route to Norway, where he intended to inspect the heavy-water plant which had been a key supplier of the abortive German atomic energy project. But at Brussels he was intercepted by Military Police, who told him only that he was urgently wanted by the Pentagon. The next day he was flown from Paris to Washington.

Toftoy had absolutely no idea why he had been suddenly recalled from Europe. He reported to General Barnes, Chief of the Research and Development Service, Technical Division, Ordnance Department, who said that General Levin Campbell, the Chief of Ordnance, wanted a few words with him. It was with a mixture of curiosity and trepidation that Toftoy entered General Campbell's office; it was unusual for a colonel to be flown from Europe for a talk with the Chief of Ordnance.

General Campbell, however, could not have been more genial. He informed Toftoy that the War Department had issued an order that all regular officers who had not served overseas must be reassigned to such duty immediately. Colonel Trichel, who had not yet served overseas, was being reassigned as Chief Ordnance Officer in the western Pacific. Trichel's post as Chief of the Ordnance Rocket Branch had to be filled. Toftoy had been selected to fill it.

Toftoy recalls glancing around the room to determine whether General Campbell might have been addressing someone else, but he saw no one besides Campbell and Barnes. When he recovered from his initial surprise, he thought of the German rocket specialists who were in Ordnance custody in Europe. According to Toftoy's recollection, he had already sent a communication from Paris recommending that three hundred of them be brought to the United States. Now that he was going to be in charge of the Army Ordnance rocket program, and fully realizing the unique help the German rocket men could give to that relatively primitive program, he set about discovering the status of the War Department General Staff plan for bringing German scientists to the United States.

Colonel Toftoy learned that the plan, details of which had been discussed within the War and State Departments as early as September 1944,* was viewed with disfavor by a large

---

* An account of the evolution and implementation of the plan which was first formalized under the code name *Overcast* and later given the code name *Paperclip* may be found in the Appendix.

segment of the American military, scientific, and bureau-cratic community. Toftoy may well have appreciated the irony of a situation in which Washington was debating the wisdom of evacuating German scientists to the United States, while in Europe itself British and Soviet Intelligence were making an intensive effort to lure those same scientists away from the Americans.

The opposition to the plan came from many sources. Certain officials of the State Department were distinctly uneasy about it, fearing that American employment of German scientists would result in an international furor; even though the scientists might not have been Nazis themselves, they had lent their talents to the Nazi government. There were also unanswered questions about visas, immigration quotas, and the legality of importing foreign scientists under the existing laws of the land. The Departments of Commerce and Labor had certain misgivings concerning patents and the laws governing alien labor. The Department of Justice was not pleased at the prospect of having to assign the FBI to the surveillance of hundreds of German scientists, some of whom might still be dedicated Nazis.

The reservations of a segment of the American scientific community were perhaps best summed up in a comment made in Europe by Dr. H. P. Robertson, the scientific leader of FIAT (Field Information Agency, Technical), an organization which was charged with interrogating high-level German scientists at *Dustbin*, a code name for a camp near Frankfurt: "In allowing the Peenemünde boys to continue their development we are perpetuating the activities of a group which, if ever allowed to return to Germany or even to communicate to Germany, can in fact contribute to Germany's ability to make war—and it is the avowed principal of the Allied powers to prevent just this from happening."

Strong objections to the plan were raised by some American military leaders. These were typified in a telephone conversation between two Army Air Forces generals which, without the knowledge of the participants, was recorded by Air Intelligence on May 26, 1945. At that time the Army Air Forces were not yet a separate service, but two AAF officers, looking toward the future development of a United States Air Force, had urged that German aerodynamicists with unique experience in developing jet planes be brought to Wright Field, Ohio, and put to work in its Engineering Division. These men were Major General Hugh Knerr and Colonel Donald L. Putt. Their intentions were discussed by the two generals, one at Wright Field and one in the Pentagon, in the following taped telephone conversation:

GENERAL A: When Gillespie was talking to Don Putt last week, Don told him of two individuals that they have under their control. They are German scientists, quite eminent, as a matter of fact. . . . They are both experts in the supersonic field. . . . Here is the proposition. As far as we are concerned, Engineering Division, we would like to have a cable sent to Don Putt having him make arrangements to send these two Joes over here for a lengthy interview.

GENERAL B: I'll tell you how that is being handled. . . . There has been quite a lot of conferences in Washington in the whole War Dept. on it, and a policy has been set upon which is that if we request anybody by name . . . G-2 [Military Intelligence] will make all the arrangements to have them brought over in custody. One of the ground rules for bringing them over is that it will be temporary and at the return of their exploitation they will be sent back to Germany.

GENERAL A: Well, Bill and I were talking about that. We think it's right. We don't want these birds over here and put ———— out of a job down at NACA, for example.

GENERAL B: Well, I held out for that. I might say that some of the other technical services were disinclined to go along with it, the Ordnance people in particular. Later yesterday afternoon I talked to Gen. Knerr and I find that these 2 individuals are pet projects of his, that when he and Don Putt were together over there they got hold of some very special test equipment and that it was flown back here. They are apparently the only guys who know how to operate it. The point I wanted to make clear, I don't know whether you can do anything about it or not, is that Gen. Knerr is personally interested in getting these guys here for more than just perfunctory exploitation.

GENERAL A: Well now, he's not interested in keeping them here permanently, is he?

GENERAL B: I don't know what you mean by permanently. I think he visualized them being here for a couple of years.

GENERAL A: Well, we'll cross that bridge when we come to it, I guess. But I'm opposed and Pop Powers is opposed, the whole War Department is opposed to the tendency on the part of some of our people to consider that the war with Germany is over, that there will never be another war with Germany and therefore open our arms and bring in German technicians and put them in our laboratories and treat them as honored guests. It hasn't come in a War Department piece of paper yet but it is to the effect that these people are on a temporary status. How temporary, I don't care, it can run into a year or a couple of years, but we've got to discourage people from thinking that this is a grand opportunity to sign up some of the Germans permanently and take them into the Army Air Forces and make them American citizens.

GENERAL B: I'm sure that's not in his mind.

GENERAL A: Okay, swell, because the State Department has said that if that's being considered they will have nothing to do with this. As long as the War Department brings them back in custody and then eventually returns them to Germany they don't want to even be annoyed by knowing what they're doing. But I know the Ordnance Department particularly is interested in the permanent employment of some of them.

GENERAL B: Yes.

GENERAL A: And I think some of our people will be.

GENERAL B: They probably will be. But we're against it here and the whole War Department is against it.[2]

The whole War Department, of course, was not against the permanent employment of a selected group of German scientists. Some key officials, such as John J. McCloy, Assistant Secretary of War, were among a minority group which vigorously backed the idea. Colonel Trichel, with the interests of the Ordnance Rocket Branch in mind, fought the opposition to bringing the V-2 specialists to the United States. So did Colonel Toftoy, after learning that he was to be Trichel's successor. Robert Patterson, Undersecretary of War, expressed his views in a memorandum to the Secretary, War Department General Staff:

> 1. I strongly favor doing everything possible to utilize fully in the prosecution of the war against Japan all information that can be obtained from Germany or any other source. The project referred to in the attached papers is a step in the right direction and should be carried out provided that measures can be taken to eliminate certain dangers inherent in this project.
> 2. These men are enemies and it must be assumed that they are capable of sabotaging our war effort. Bringing them to this country raises delicate questions, including the possible strong resentment of the American public, who might misunderstand the purpose of bringing them here and the treatment accorded them. Taking such a step without consultation with our Allies, including the Russians, might lead to complications. Before any action is taken I suggest that the matter be referred to Assistant Secretary McCloy for necessary coordination with the Informal Policy Committee on Germany or the State-War-Navy Coordinating Committee.
> 3. It is also my feeling that the information from these men should be obtained to the maximum possible within Germany and only those should be brought here whose particular work requires their presence here. It is assumed that such men will be under strict surveillance while here and that they will be returned to Germany as soon as possible.[3]

The War Department General Staff worked out a plan that received the approval of the Joint Chiefs of Staff on July 6, 1945, with the agreement of the British Chiefs of Staff. The plan had to go all the way up to Cordell Hull, Secretary of State, for final approval, which Hull gave. On

July 20, the Acting Secretary of the Joint Chiefs of Staff sent out a memorandum:

> 1. The following code word has been assigned by Joint Security Control, effective 19 July 1945, with a classification of SECRET:
>
> OVERCAST   Project of exploiting German civilian scientists, and its establishment under the Chief, Military Intelligence Service, on an island in Boston Harbor at a camp formerly known as Fort Standish.

*Overcast* was put forth as a short-term project; "the purpose . . . should be understood to be *temporary* military exploitation . . . particularly that which will assist in shortening the Japanese war." To those Germans who could be proved not to be war criminals or virulent Nazis, contracts for six months of work in the United States would be offered. The entire project envisioned bringing a maximum of 350 men, without their families, to the United States, and they would be paid "a modest per diem from funds under the control of the Secretary of War." Of the 350 men who could be imported by the various branches of the American armed forces, the Ordnance Department was authorized to import no more than one hundred for rocket work.

On July 25, the new chief of the Army Ordnance Rocket Branch, Colonel Holger Toftoy was issued orders to proceed to Europe "with regard to the selection of certain German scientific personnel." The choice of Toftoy for this assignment was a fortunate one. He was flexible, willing to listen to the human problems of those under his command before issuing orders, and "a man with a big heart . . . a nice guy," in Wernher von Braun's later opinion. The plain fact of the matter was that Toftoy would need all of his human qualities and powers of persuasion in dealing with the German rocket men, for the deal that he had been authorized to offer them was not attractive in comparison with the inducements offered by the British and the Russians.

Peenemünde had once employed some five thousand scientists and technicians. Colonel Toftoy could offer contracts to only one hundred of them. The contracts were for short-term employment, offered no possibility of future American citizenship, called for modest salaries averaging six dollars a day, and stipulated that the men would have to leave their families behind in Germany. The Russians were offering houses, inflated salaries, employment to as many men as wanted it, and the chance of continuing rocket work in Germany itself. Even the British offered to billet the rocket men and their families in first-class hotels if they would accept employment in England.

Colonel Toftoy flew from Washington to Paris and then took a train to the small town of Witzenhausen in central Germany, where eighty of the key rocket specialists and their families were lodged in a two-story country schoolhouse; the remainder were billeted in the nearby village of Eschwege. At Witzenhausen, Staver and Dr. Porter, as the latter reported, had already compiled, as he had reported to Paris Ordnance Headquarters on July 9, 1945, "a tentative organization . . . and lists of scientific personnel and technicians . . . on the assumption that there would be set up in the United States an organization primarily of former members of the Elektromechanische Werke to develop, design, build, and test new types of rocket missiles. These selections were made by Dr. von Braun and the section leaders in consultation with Major Staver and the undersigned [Dr. Porter]."

Von Braun had told Dr. Porter that five hundred men would be needed. According to Dr. Porter, "Recognizing the problems that would be involved, I insisted that we cut the list to about three hundred." When Colonel Toftoy arrived in Witzenhausen in early August 1945 with the authorization to choose one hundred men for short-term employment in the United States, von Braun was clearly disappointed. So was Major Staver, especially when he learned that the men would be asked to go to the United States without their families. This posed a major problem for Staver and Toftoy. The latter inspected the Witzenhausen schoolhouse where the rocket men and their families were lodged and saw on the first floor a small kitchen with a two-burner electric stove, two toilets, but no bathtubs. Beds were lined up in rows so close together that Toftoy had difficulty in squeezing from one end of the long room to the other. There was no privacy; babies, grandparents, young married couples lived together under conditions that Toftoy, who had a wife and two children of his own, found "deplorable."

When he approached Walther Riedel and told him that he was being considered as one of the rocket experts to be selected to go to the United States, without his family, Riedel drew him into a side room in the Witzenhausen schoolhouse and pointed to six huge black trunks. Riedel opened one of them. It was jammed with reichsmarks, and he began throwing fistfuls of this worthless paper money into the air.

"Money, Colonel," Toftoy recalls Riedel saying. "We have plenty of that, but it won't buy anything. I can't feed my family with it. But if I stay here, I can fix a radio or a bicycle for a farmer and he'll give me some apples in return. What will happen to my family if I go to America? I can send them American money, but money can't buy apples or bread or milk in Germany."

Major Staver, in a later report to Ordnance in the Pentagon, observed: "Contrary to what some Ordnance officers expected, these Germans were not at first anxious to come as a group, and many of them were undecided for several weeks." When Staver eventually persuaded one of the Peenemünde department heads to sign the *Overcast* contract, the latter's wife, upon learning that her husband was going to leave her behind, attempted to swallow a capsule containing cyanide. Her husband knocked the capsule out of her hand, cutting his own hands on the broken glass and narrowly missing having the cyanide enter his own blood stream.

The case of Frau Riedel was an extreme one, but the problem of the rocket men's families was nevertheless serious. The men were human beings first and V-2 experts second. A compromise solution to the problem was worked out. While the men were in the United States, their families would be cared for by the United States Army at a former German Army cavalry barracks at Landshut, Bavaria. It is probable, however, that even with this concession not all of the key rocket specialists would have signed the *Overcast* contract but for the driving determination of one man to keep the core of the Peenemünde organization working together.

In later years Dr. Porter was asked who was responsible for the idea of bringing von Braun and his group to the United States. In characteristically succinct fashion, Dr. Porter replied: "Probably von Braun himself as much as anyone." Following von Braun's lead, a balanced, integrated rocket team of creative scientists and engineers was selected and persuaded to continue its work in the United States.

"List I," as it was called, had to dispense with technicians, administrators, and production men. Only those men whose skills could not be duplicated in the United States were chosen for *Overcast*. "List I," however, did not work out to the exact figure of one hundred that Colonel Toftoy had been authorized to import under *Overcast*. The minimal figure for a complete team of rocket experts came to 115. Toftoy took it upon himself to overstep the limits imposed upon him by the War Department and offer employment to an extra fifteen men.

Through August and September 1945, as the signatures to the *Overcast* contract were obtained by Colonel Toftoy,

Dr. Porter, and Major Staver, the latter learned, through the Peenemünde grapevine at the Witzenhausen schoolhouse, that the Russians were definitely moving ahead with a rocket program at Nordhausen, without the assistance of the leading German experts under American control. On August 10, 1945, Karl Otto Fleischer, who had located the Peenemünde documents for Major Staver, gave him this report:

> We have the following news about the Russian organization of rocket affairs in Germany:
> The Russians have organized three groups: first in Bleicherode, second in Mittelwerke, third in Peenemünde. They name all these groups together "Institution Rabe."
> The leader of the Bleicherode group is a Russian major. The Bleicherode group consists of about 50 people. They have a drawing office and a small workshop in Bleicherode. Their administration is in the house of "Kaliwerke Bleicherode." They try to rebuild and reproduce parts of A4 and other rocket developments. They get the double German rations and are paid.[4]

On August 15, 1945, Diplom Ingenieur Elmi reported to Staver:

> "I had been for several days in Russian occupied zone around Bleicherode to pick up my baggage, which had been left there. At this occasion I spoke to an old collaborator, whose name I give for internal use only, in order to prevent him from personal difficulties by the Russians. He told me, that the Russians intend to develop a big rocket for a normal range of 3000 miles and that they are needing specialists with knowledge of the theory of flight-mechanics and control equipment. He told me that the Russians set big prices for getting over to Russian area Prof. v. Braun and Dr. Steinhoff.[5]

On September 15, 1945, Dr. Martin Schilling, who had been in charge of testing at Peenemünde, reported to Staver:

An engineer of the department of Mr. Hüter tried to get his family out of the Russian zone at Haynrode near Bleicherode. He returned about a week ago and told me that his wife already knew about the American intentions of further development, etc. He said that also the complete List I and the conditions of the contract are known on the Russian side. . . . A few days ago I was informed that a man came down from Lehesten to Witzenhausen and had reported that the testing of A4 tubes was running again at Lehesten/Örtelsbruch since the 6th of September. This report seems to be true, as a number of about 100 tubes still was available in Örtelsbruch, and the noise of burning tubes is very characteristic and can be heard all over the town. There seems to be a connection between the tests at Lehesten and the assembly work in the Mittelwerke as in former days.[6]

There was, of course, a definite connection: V-2's were being manufactured by Germans under Soviet supervision at the *Mittelwerke* and their motors fired in static tests at Lehesten. Major Staver knew the large Lehesten installation well; before the Americans had withdrawn from Thuringia, he had been the first American to test-fire a V-2 motor there.

The work at Lehesten and the *Mittelwerke*, however, was being done by German specialists of the second rank. As of September 1945, Soviet Intelligence had been unable to induce any of the top-ranking Peenemünde men to leave American custody and return to the Soviet Zone. These men, of course, could have done so had they wanted to; they were civilians and there was no way that the Americans could detain them indefinitely against their will.

Dr. Porter, who was aware that the Russians, British, and French were offering jobs to German scientists, asked one of the leading Peenemünde figures why he and his colleagues appeared to prefer to accept the relatively modest American offer. According to Dr. Porter, he received this reply: "We despise the French, we are mortally afraid of the Soviets, we do not believe that the British can afford us, so that leaves the Americans."

German fear of the Soviets, and dislike for the Soviet system, was a very real thing in the summer of 1945 and a major factor in the inability of Soviet Intelligence to lure the leading rocket men away from Witzenhausen at any price. The greatest obstacle to the successful completion of *Overcast* by Major Staver and Dr. Porter was created, not by the Russians, but by the British.

In Washington, on July 6, 1945, the War Department General Staff *Overcast* plan had been approved with the agreement of the British Chiefs of Staff. The British had agreed that the Americans could import from Germany 350 German scientists for work in the United States. *Overcast*, however, did not specify which scientists would be imported; this was left to field operators in Europe such as Major Staver, who had to obtain the voluntary signatures of the Germans themselves to the *Overcast* contracts. While Staver was attempting to do this, British Intelligence launched an intensive effort to persuade German scientists not to sign the American contract but to accept employment in the United Kingdom instead. In particular, British Intelligence concentrated on a group of men it had been following closely since the Sandys investigation of April 1943—the German V-2 experts.

The British effort centered around *Backfire*. This was the code name for a British project which had as its ostensible purpose the complete technical analysis of V-2. At a former German Navy artillery range near Cuxhaven on the North Sea, British rocket experts interrogated key Peenemünde personnel, who then, under observation, repeated their former roles in the actual launchings of a few V-2's. The missiles were fired into the North Sea. German rocket experts were released from American custody to participate in *Backfire*, on the understanding that the British would promptly return them when the project was completed.

Colonel Toftoy and Major Staver were among the large

group of Allied observers who attended the *Backfire* launchings. Both of them agreed that the project was worth while, since its findings would be shared by Great Britain and the United States. The difficulty arose when they discovered that the V-2 personnel were being urged by the British not to return to American custody but to accept employment in the United Kingdom instead.

"The British pulled a sneaky on us," Major Staver later reported. "Partly by chicanery and partly through clever staff work, they were able to gain possession of many of the most important German engineers who they utilized on Project *Backfire*. They resorted to various technicalities to delay the release of these men to the U. S. Army. . . ."

According to Dr. Porter, "The only real competition for people during the first few months after the end of the war was with the British. . . . they managed to spirit away the five German engineers I had selected to work on the V-2 tests in the U.S.A., and we didn't get them back until after the British tests at Cuxhaven were completed."

It took a considerable amount of prodding on the part of the War Department and the State Department to induce the British to return all of the German rocket experts from Cuxhaven. None of them had signed the proffered British contracts. The British rocket people, however, obtained a return concession from Ordnance. The British would be permitted to fly six of the key Peenemünde men to London for the purpose of technical investigations lasting about ten days.

In mid-August, von Braun, Dornberger, and four Peenemünde department chiefs were flown to a camp near Wimbledon, where they were billeted. They were then driven daily, through streets where they could plainly see the destruction caused by V-2, to the Ministry of Supply.

"I must admit that I thought the British might be unfriendly to me," von Braun later remarked, "but I found

I was wrong the first day. I was interviewed by Sir Alwyn Crow, the man in charge of developing British rockets. I was hardly inside his office before we were engaged in friendly shop talk."

Major Staver, who was in a position to be less diplomatic than von Braun in discussing what had transpired in Sir Alwyn Crow's office, put a different interpretation on the "friendly shop talk." "The entire discussions," Staver later reported, "centered on how the British might form a research group of the German scientists; would not these men who were planning to leave for the United States reconsider as the British might have more to offer them; if not, who would be left behind who would be important for such research; and would it not be possible to have the German group work in a joint British-American project possibly in Canada? . . . All these questions were discussed at length, and not one single technical question was asked of any one of the Germans. There were no technical interrogations as reported by the British."

In any case, the key Peenemünde men had signed American contracts before going to London, and nothing that happened there caused them to renege. Here, of course, von Braun and his associates were thinking of the future rather than of short-term material benefits. They realized that only the United States and the Soviet Union had the resources to undertake a really big, long-term rocket development program.

Von Braun and the four department chiefs were returned to American custody in Germany. General Dornberger, who probably knew more about the V-2 program than anyone else, was kept behind. The British refused all American demands for his release, but not because the British intended to use Dornberger in their rocket program. They intended to hang him.

Through the summer of 1945, the Allies rounded up major war criminals who would be tried at Nuremberg. The British, for understandable reasons, were intent on trying and hanging the man responsible for the random firing of V-2's at the civilian population of London. This man was the Special Commissioner for V-weapons, Hans Kammler, but British agents were unable to locate him.

General Dornberger, who had his own personal reasons for wanting to know what had become of the Special Commissioner, knew that Kammler would never be found. Dornberger's own contacts, which in this one case were better than those of British Intelligence, tracked down the solution to the mystery of what had happened to him.

Kammler had not hidden in the Ettal monastery or anywhere else. For reasons never clearly established, he had left the Bavarian Alps and gone to Prague. He was in Prague as the Red Army began to clear the east and west banks of the Moldau River and drive on the city. SS resistance was fierce. Prague, in fact, did not fall until May 9, 1945, two days after the signing of the general German surrender at Rheims.

According to eyewitness reports given to General Dornberger, Kammler was in a bunker in the smoking center of Prague on the morning of May 9. Twenty-two SS men in the bunker were attacked by six hundred Czech partisans. Kammler emerged from the bunker, laughing and firing a machine pistol at the onrushing Czechs. As he had been ordered to do, SS Major Starck followed his chief at ten paces. Starck saw that the situation was at last hopeless and fired a burst from his own machine pistol into the back of Kammler's head.

The British, in the absence of Hans Kammler, were still determined to put someone in the dock at Nuremberg as responsible for the V-2 bombardment of Greater London and Antwerp. For this role, General Dornberger was selected. He was issued a chocolate-colored uniform with the white letters PW stenciled on its back and taken under guard to the "Cage" near Windermere Bridge. Dornberger encountered familiar faces there, like Field Marshals von Rundstedt and von Brauchitsch.

General Dornberger's personal interrogator was a tall, friendly major with a handlebar mustache. Major Scotland genially informed Dornberger that Sir Harley Shawcross, the chief British prosecutor at Nuremberg, was constructing a case against the man responsible for firing V-2's at British civilians. Since Special Commissioner Kammler was not available, Dornberger would stand trial in his place. The trial would be lengthy, but also fair.

Dornberger protested being arrested and held for trial. He pointed out to Major Scotland that he had had no command function over the actual firings of V-2; that the British and American air attacks on German cities had caused more civilian deaths than V-2 had; and that while he, Dornberger, had played a major role in the development of the long-range rocket, any attempt to try and execute individuals responsible for developing new weapons would have validity only if the scientists, engineers, and military leaders of all countries, including Great Britain and the United States, were given similar treatment.

Major Scotland listened to General Dornberger's argument with patience, but observed that Dornberger's future was a matter over which only Sir Harley Shawcross and the British Cabinet had jurisdiction. Major Scotland suggested that Dornberger pass the time until his trial by giving the British rocket people a complete account of V-2 and its future possibilities. Dornberger refused and was then transferred to a castle in Wales which served as a detention center for high-ranking German officers.

As Dornberger awaited a bleak and uncertain future in Wales, the 115 Peenemünde men who had signed contracts to work in the United States were at last reas-

sembled in Germany and processed for their journey overseas. This group represented the core of the Peenemünde
organization and was the world's first and only integrated
team of rocket specialists. The British and the Russians had
failed to obtain the services of any of the leading Peenemünde men.

Soviet Intelligence, however, had not completely failed in
its search for a man with the creative ability to lead a future
development team. They found him in Helmut Gröttrup,
a blond, intense young man who was, in von Braun's estimation, "a brilliant engineer."

Gröttrup had not been one of the Peenemünde leaders,
but he had been close to the top as deputy to Dr. Ernst Steinhoff, the department chief in charge of guidance and control.
Along with von Braun and Klaus Riedel, Gröttrup had
been arrested by the SS and thrown into the Stettin jail in
March 1944. He had been released with the others at General
Dornberger's insistence and had eventually made the journey
from Peenemünde to Nordhausen-Bleicherode. Gröttrup
had been interrogated by Major Staver and Walt Hausz of
the General Electric Hermes Project in Bleicherode on
May 23, 1945. He and his wife were later among those considered important enough to be evacuated from Nordhausen, just before the Red Army occupied it, to Witzenhausen in the American Zone. Helmut Gröttrup was offered
a contract for work in the United States, but he did not
sign it, nor did he and his wife remain in Witzenhausen.

Gröttrup's wife, Irmgard, kept a diary which was later published as a book, and in it she explained why she and her husband left American custody:

> As for politics, they are the end! I have yet to meet a politi-
> cian who would say: "After you!" When hard facts are in-
> volved, civilization is thrown to the winds—first come first
> served is the rule. The Americans were acting on that prin-
> ciple when, after ceding Thuringia—and with it Peenemünde

which had been evacuated in the path of the advancing Russians—they grabbed Wernher von Braun, Hüter, Schilling, Steinhoff, Gröttrup and other leading rocket experts. We were housed at Witzenhausen and interrogated. After weeks passed Helmut was handed a contract offering him a transfer to the U.S.A. without his family, a contract terminable by one signatory only: the United States Army. Since we wanted to remain in Germany, we moved back to the Russian Zone. I returned to my farm and Helmut to his work. The Russians promised that we should be able to stay in Germany and go on with our work.

Helmut Gröttrup was placed in charge of the Russian-sponsored *Institut Rabe,** a cover name for the resumption of rocket design and production in Nordhausen and Bleicherode. The *Mittelwerke* itself was renamed *Zentralwerke* (Central Works). Soon Gröttrup had gathered under him a development team of two hundred men that was not in the class of von Braun's group but was capable and could draw on the experience of more than five thousand skilled technicians. While still in his early thirties, Helmut Gröttrup, who had been a deputy department chief at Peenemünde, was now in charge of an entire rocket project, equal in status to a von Braun or a Dornberger. And the Russians provided the Gröttrups with a house, a car, food, servant privileges, and a good salary. The Gröttrups also had a firm promise from the Soviet authorities in Nordhausen that, unlike von Braun and his group, they would never have to leave Germany.

* *Rabe* was an abbreviation for *Raketenbetrieb* (Rocket Enterprise) *Bleicherode.*

# 16

## On ice in the desert

On September 29, 1945, seven Germans, representing the advance guard of the V-2 specialists selected for the *Overcast* project, arrived at Fort Strong, an island in Boston Harbor. Technically speaking, however, the former Peenemünde men did not enter the United States at all. They had no entry permits and did not pass through normal immigration channels, but were classified as "wards of the Army" and were solely the Army's responsibility.

The seven Germans were met at Fort Strong by Major James Hamill. On the basis of his work in Europe and his ability to cope with unusual situations, Colonel Toftoy had chosen Hamill to handle the rocket experts. Six of the new arrivals* were transferred from Fort Strong to the Aberdeen Proving Ground, Maryland, where they were put to work translating, cataloguing, and evaluating the fourteen tons of V-2 documents that Major Staver had evacuated from the abandoned mine in Dörnten. The seventh was Wernher von Braun, for whom a different destination had been planned.

The entry of the former technical director of the German rocket program into the United States as a "ward of the

* Erich Neubert, Theodore Poppel, August Schulze, Eberhard Rees, William Jungert, and Walter Schwidetzsky.

Army" six months after the end of World War II was not auspicious. Von Braun was having trouble with his broken arm and shoulder, which were still in a cast, and he was hit by a sudden attack of hepatitis, which later caused him to be hospitalized. There was no announcement that he and his associates were in the United States, because the project that had brought them here was classified secret.

Major Hamill and von Braun were driven to Washington for talks with Ordnance officers in the Pentagon. Then they embarked on a long train journey to Fort Bliss, near El Paso, Texas, where Army Ordnance had based its rocket operation. Von Braun was thirty-three, and his heavily accented English had been described by an interrogator at Garmisch as "fairly lucid." Hamill was twenty-seven and had a fair command of German. The two men came to know each other quite well on the trip to El Paso, for, as Hamill recalls, "the Department of the Army imposed only one rule on us and that was that we were to be in each other's presence twenty-four hours a day."

When their train reached St. Louis, von Braun and Hamill were rerouted into a Pullman car that happened to be occupied by wounded veterans of the 82nd and 101st Airborne Divisions. Major Hamill thought it wise to move von Braun and himself to another Pullman. At Texarkana, a civilian in the car engaged von Braun in friendly conversation, at one point asking him where he was from and what business he was in. To Hamill's great relief, von Braun replied that he was from Switzerland and "in the steel business."

Upon their arrival at Fort Bliss, von Braun and Hamill did not receive a warm welcome. "The Commanding General was a combat infantryman who had been wounded several times in both World Wars," Hamill later recalled. "In addition to that he had not been apprised of our coming. There was one happy aspect to this whole situation; at least we could arrange for separate rooms now that we were on a military reservation. However, at about 11:30 P.M. I was awakened by the post executive officer and the provost marshal and was ordered to move over and rejoin my traveling companion . . . someone thoughtfully provided us with some good Juárez rum and we toasted the arrival in the Southwest of the first prisoner of peace." [1]

Fifty-five more Peenemünde engineers arrived at Fort Bliss on December 2, 1945. By February 1946 there were 111 Germans attached to an organization headed by Major Hamill called Office of the Chief of Ordnance, Research and Development Service, Suboffice (Rocket). This title and the personnel attached to it were the only things about the organization that could be considered impressive.

The Ordnance Department had laid the groundwork for an American guided missile program, but it was not a heavily financed priority undertaking. Nazi Germany was finished. So was Japan. The United States alone, so it was believed, possessed the atom bomb. Another war seemed remote, and great expenditures of the taxpayers' money on guided missile developments did not seem justified.

There were no fantastic test stands, wind tunnels, laboratories, and rows of machine tools at Fort Bliss. Ordnance had been given some funds to develop military rockets, but on nothing approaching the scale of Peenemünde. And if von Braun and his team had entertained the notion that they were going to be able to turn their talents to space projects in the United States, they were quickly disabused of it. As far as an American space program went in 1946, von Braun has described it succinctly: "There wasn't any."

Major Hamill replied to one set of detailed administrative instructions from Washington in these terms: "This memorandum is written in long hand due to the fact that the undersigned is the only member of this organization with typing ability and due to a sprained left wrist, this ability has been severely curtailed. . . . Where is the money for my Boston Tea Party?" Major Hamill and Colonel Toftoy had to improvise and scrounge to find living quarters and laboratory space for their charges. The annex of the William Beaumont General Hospital on the Fort Bliss reservation was converted into a laboratory, and the Germans were housed in two-story wooden barracks nearby.

On March 13, 1946, the code name *Paperclip* was substituted for *Overcast* because the housing project at Landshut, Bavaria, where the families of the men who were in the United States were living, had picked up the nickname "Camp Overcast." Under the designation *Paperclip,* the project continued as before, with the exception that the contracts of the Germans were extended for an indefinite period and they were told that they could bring their families to the United States.

The Germans, because they were not American citizens, were not permitted to participate directly in the American guided missile program. One of the old Peenemünde team jokingly referred to *Operation Paperclip* as "Operation Icebox." And the team *was* pretty much kept on ice during its early period in Texas. But within the limits imposed by the thinking of the times and the funds available, the Germans did make a great contribution to the start of an American missile program.

"They were probably the most closely watched group of civilians in our history," Major Hamill later observed, "but they didn't gripe about it. There were some petty incidents, some personal rivalries, but I never had any serious trouble with them. They seemed completely loyal and they were also the hardest-working group I ever saw."

The Germans' work was limited to two principal areas. Ordnance made their knowledge available to interrogators of the Army Air Forces, the Navy, their civilian contractors, and any other agency with a legitimate interest in guided missiles. And the Germans assisted in firing the Nordhausen V-2's, which was done to give Ordnance experience that would be helpful in the design and handling of future American missiles. Ordnance also invited universities and government agencies to place instruments in the V-2's for research of the upper atmosphere.

The launchings took place eighty miles from El Paso at the White Sands Proving Ground, 125 by 40 miles of gleaming white gypsum desert in New Mexico. White Sands was populated by lizards, white mice, and rattlesnakes and was walled in on the west by the five-thousand-foot high stone mass of the Organ Mountains.

Through the efforts of Colonel Toftoy and Colonel Harold Turner, the White Sands post commander, some rocket facilities were constructed in this desolate wasteland: a few clapboard one-story barracks, a single 40-foot-deep rocket firing pit, near it a massive concrete blockhouse, and one large corrugated steel building where the Nordhausen V-2's were assembled.

The latter was a formidable job. The V-2 components and subassemblies were rusty and dried out and had taken considerable rough handling in their long journey from the *Mittelwerke*. The *Overcast* selections had not included production men and technicians and, as Dr. Richard Porter commented, "My company, General Electric, had to provide U.S. draftsmen, administrative assistants, and technicians to help von Braun and his people through their difficult early days. . . ."

But the V-2's were reassembled and the first one was fired at a static test on March 14, 1946. Then, on June 28, 1946, a V-2, fully instrumented for upper-air research, roared up above the white sands and the serrated peaks of the Organ Mountains to a height of sixty-seven miles. More shoots followed, the great majority of them successful and rewarding. One of them, however, came close to being a disaster of international proportions and revealing to the world what the U. S. Army was doing at the White Sands Proving Ground.

At 7 P.M. on May 29, 1947, a V-2 was fired over the Organ Mountains. It was to land in an uninhabited spot in the desert. Instead, it veered south and headed across the Rio Grande toward Juárez, Mexico, where a fiesta happened to be in progress. Fortunately, it missed the crowded center of Juárez and landed in a cemetery. No Mexicans were killed or wounded by the errant V-2, which perhaps accounted for the fact that the Mexican government did not make an issue of the incident. "The classic remark to come out of the whole affair," according to Hamill, "was made by an overenthusiastic junior officer who proudly announced that we had become the first American outfit to fire a guided missile into foreign territory. The fact that we never received a reprimand for this transgression was due to Colonel Toftoy's excellent defense council work in Washington, but also to the fact that General Homer, the Fort Bliss commanding officer, visited Juárez and on his own extended the apologies of the United States government."

A complex and effective range safety system was then instituted at White Sands, and the firing and study of the V-2's continued as a secret undertaking. But it was no secret to the relatively few people who were aware that von Braun and his group were in Texas that the United States, now that it had the world's leading guided missile team, was not making the maximum possible use of it. Major Robert Staver, before leaving the Army and returning to private business, visited Fort Bliss and reported back to the Research and Development Service in the Pentagon that the Peenemünde group should be given a more challenging and far-reaching assignment than "helping with the firing of a few V-2's in the New Mexico desert."

Von Braun himself later observed: "Frankly, we were

disappointed with what we found in this country during our first year or so. At Peenemünde, we'd been coddled. Here they were counting pennies. The armed forces were being demobilized and everybody wanted military expenditures curtailed. . . ."

Von Braun often wondered what had become of the members of the huge Peenemünde organization who had not come to the United States. He was happy to discover that General Dornberger had not been tried as a war criminal, after all. The case against the general had been quietly dropped. In Dornberger's own opinion, this was because it would have been impossible to sustain a charge involving the civilian deaths caused by V-2 in the light of the atom bombs dropped without warning on the populations of Hiroshima and Nagasaki. Dornberger, however, while he was never tried, was also not immediately released from detention in the castle in Wales. It was not until July 1947 that he was permitted to leave England and return to American custody in Germany. At that time he was not asked to rejoin his old Peenemünde team in Texas because it was felt that placing a former German general in charge of the civilian engineers would create public relations problems. Instead, Dornberger was hired by the Air Force and served as a guided missile consultant at Wright Field, Ohio.*

But what had happened to the thousands of other rocket specialists left behind in Germany, most of them in the Soviet Zone?** By the summer of 1946, U. S. Military Intelligence had established two facts about them. They had not been taken to the Soviet Union. They were working on

---

* Dornberger left the employ of the Air Force in 1950 and joined the Bell Aircraft Company in Buffalo, New York. As of June 1964, he was vice-president and chief scientist of the Bell Aerosystems Company, a division of Bell Aerosystems Corporation.

** The largest number of German rocket specialists to be concentrated in the United States at one time was 127, including the 115 on the original *Overcast* list.

rocket projects in Nordhausen and Bleicherode which, despite all Soviet attempts at secrecy, were obviously major undertakings.

On June 24, 1946, Major Hamill received a confidential memorandum from the Pentagon in which he was asked to obtain from von Braun the answers to some disturbing questions, such as von Braun's estimate of the capabilities of the rocket men in the Soviet Zone and how long it might take them to complete work on such long-term projects as the A-9, A-10, and A-11 intercontinental missiles. Hamill transmitted eleven pages of von Braun's answers to the War Department, including this response to the question that most disturbed Military Intelligence:

There is no doubt that the bulk of the most capable members of the Peenemünde group are in the United States now. There are, however, many very good former Peenemünde experts working for the Russians, too. In the opinion of Professor von Braun the two most capable of these men . . . are: Dipl. Ing. Helmut Gröttrup . . . and Engineer Martin. These two men are, according to the best available information, in charge of the Russian project—new development projects (Gröttrup) and A-4 manufacture in Nordhausen (Martin).

As regards future developments such as A-9, A-10, and A-11 Gröttrup is to be considered a very able and clever leader of a development group. . . . Compared with the situation found by the German group in the U.S. he has the advantage of having almost complete test stands and a complete production plant, which can easily be set going with the available number of trained members of these plants. . . . Many of these people were familiar with the general outline of the new projects A-9, A-10, and A-11. Prof. von Braun says in this connection, "I am convinced, without trying to hide the light of our Fort Bliss group under a bushel, that Gröttrup will be able to build up gradually a capable group out of former Peenemünde people that can successfully continue these developments for the Russians."

This 1946 opinion of von Braun's, which amounted to a warning, was noted but not acted upon by the American authorities. First, there was no effective action they could take to prevent the Soviets from carrying out rocket research in East Germany, though the resumption of military research in any part of occupied Germany was specifically forbidden by four-power agreement. Then, in 1946, the general opinion of Soviet technical ability was not high. And as long as the Russians made no move to take German specialists to the Soviet Union, the activities at Nordhausen and Bleicherode appeared to have no long-term significance.

As October 1946 came, the von Braun group was doing nothing more than testing V-2's at White Sands, while Helmut Gröttrup and his associates were still working in their old, familiar surroundings. The Russians had instituted no *Overcast* operation of their own. If they had not done so sixteen months after the end of the war, there appeared no reason for Helmut Gröttrup, U. S. Military Intelligence, or anyone else to believe they ever would.

# 17

## The trains were on time

October 22, 1946, was a busy day for Helmut Gröttrup and his key assistants in Nordhausen. They were summoned to a conference by General Gaidukov, the Russian overseer of *Institut Rabe* and the *Zentralwerke*. Plans for future rocket development in the Soviet Union, in which Gröttrup and his assistants were assured they would continue to play a major role, were thoroughly discussed. The talks lasted all day and continued until nightfall. Then General Gaidukov invited the tired Germans to relax as his personal guests at a banquet. Some of the men would have preferred to return home, but none of them cared to refuse Gaidukov's invitation. Vodka and good cheer flowed, and the banquet lasted well beyond midnight.

Gröttrup's wife, Irmgard, who had never quite come to terms with being a rocket widow, waited impatiently for her husband to come home, gave up in annoyance, and went to bed. She was awakened by a telephone call shortly after 3 A.M.

The caller was not Helmut, but an anxious, almost hysterical woman. "Are they taking you to Russia, too?" she asked.

"Are you drunk?" Frau Gröttrup said. "What a time for practical jokes!" She slammed down the telephone.

But other calls followed, and the alarming pattern of their questions—"Are you being sent to Russia? The soldiers are already here!"—indicated that whatever was happening was not a joke.

Then Frau Gröttrup heard the rumble of trucks, ran to the window, and saw vehicles with red stars parked in a circle around her house. Soldiers armed with tommy-guns were piling out of them. The front door quivered under the pounding of fists, and the doorbell rang without letup. Rather than have the door broken down, Frau Gröttrup opened it and the soldiers rushed past her. They were followed by a polite, smiling officer who said simply that the Gröttrups were going to Russia, immediately.

Irmgard Gröttrup, cursing her husband's absence, received permission to telephone him at the banquet. It had been held, of course, to concentrate the rocket specialists in one place and to prevent them from learning what was going on at their homes until it was too late. Not until the banquet was ending and all of the families had been taken into custody by the Secret Police did General Gaidukov inform Helmut Gröttrop and his assistants that they and the entire rocket operation in the Nordhausen area were being shipped to the Soviet Union.

When his wife reached him by telephone around four o'clock in the morning, Helmut Gröttrup had just learned of the Soviet intentions. "There's nothing I can do," he said in answer to his wife's agitated questions and protests. "Nothing at all. I'm in a room full of officers here. I may be home tonight, but perhaps I won't be able to see you again until we're on the train. Just try to keep calm."

Russian soldiers ranged through the Gröttrups' house with sacks and packing crates. Within an hour they had stripped the house bare, except for bits of broken china and glass strewn about the floors. Irmgard Gröttrup, numb with cold and fear, was driven to a railroad siding with her two small children and their nurse. When Frau Gröttrup saw familiar, anxious faces peering out of the windows of a long line of old railway carriages, she realized that her predicament, while bad enough, was not unique.

When the Russians finally got around to their own version of *Overcast*,[1] they pulled it off in the grand manner. Unlike the Americans, the Russians engaged in no lengthy selection process. Nor did they quibble about families accompanying the German scientists, ask the scientists themselves whether they wanted to work in the Soviet Union, or check on their past affiliations with Nazi organizations. For almost a year, General Ivan Serov's Secret Police had quietly compiled lists of those men in the Russian Zone who might help the Soviet Union to catch up with Western science. Then, in one night's work, the Secret Police swept up some five thousand specialists all over eastern Germany. With no questions asked, twenty thousand Germans, including families, were jammed into waiting railway cars.

The Soviet Secret Police struck swiftly, with a practiced hand and an impersonal thoroughness. Whole family units, from babies to doddering grandparents to pets, were sent to the railroad siding, along with household goods (the Russians brought along the stone jars of sauerkraut in the Gröttrups' cellar). Anyone who had the misfortune to be visiting one of the hapless specialists on the night of October 22 was taken, despite protests that he did not know one end of a slide rule from another. The Soviet Secret Police was broad-minded about the operation. The officer detailed to bring a Dr. Ronger and his wife to the train greeted the news that the wife had died three days earlier with a shrug and a suggestion: "Take any woman you like with you. You can always get married in Moscow." In some cases, the Secret Police was thoughtful enough to include the mistresses of the German specialists in the train consignment, omitting the legal wives.

In addition to Helmut Gröttrup and two hundred of his key assistants, hundreds of other rocket experts from the test station at Lehesten and the firms of Siemens, Telefunken, Lorenz, and the Walter Works in Prague were caught in General Serov's net. The Soviet Secret Police did not limit its activities to rocket experts, however. The German aircraft industry, 80 percent of which had been concentrated in Silesia to escape the British and American heavy bombers, represented an even richer haul. Two thousand jet aircraft specialists from Junkers, Heinkel, Focke-Wulf, and government experimental stations were taken. So were submarine experts, and optical specialists from the Zeiss Works at Jena. Every German who could be of use in strengthening the military and industrial capacity of the Soviet Union was taken. The majority of the Germans, faced with Red Army soldiers armed with tommy-guns, allowed themselves to be herded into the trains heading east. Those few who protested or tried to escape were forcibly placed on the trains by the Secret Police.

The Gröttrups' train, in which they were assigned three compartments, began to move toward Frankfurt-on-the-Oder and the Russian border at Brest Litovsk at three o'clock on the afternoon of October 23. Helmut Gröttrup turned one of the compartments into an office, in which he typed up a strong protest against the deportations. The protest was later rejected in Moscow by the Minister of Munitions with the comment that the Potsdam Agreement had entiled the Soviet Union to deport five thousand Germans to help with the reconstruction of facilities destroyed by the Nazi armies; if Gröttrup and his associates did not want to participate in this and other work of a scientific nature, they could be turned over to the Ministry of Mines for work in the mines of the Ural Mountains.

The ninety-two trains bearing the German specialists and their families began to arrive in a snow-covered Moscow on October 27. Most of the trains remained on the railroad sidings for days, then continued on separate journeys to various distant parts of the Soviet Union. One group of rocket experts was sent to Gorodomilia, a large island on a lake two hundred miles northwest of Moscow. Helmut Gröttrup and his key assistants, however, debarked in the capital and were taken to a well-to-do suburb near Datschen, where Soviet stage and screen stars and the ballerina Ulanova had their homes.

The Gröttrups were assigned a six-room dacha with a staff of Russian servants (who marveled at their Frigidaire and Hoover vacuum cleaner). Their BMW car was shipped in from Thuringia. Nearby, an empty factory once used for producing drilling machinery, whose contents had been moved beyond the Urals when the German armies had neared Moscow, was converted into a rocket research center.

Gröttrup and the other German rocket men quickly formed a poor opinion of the inept way the Russians were going about their rocket project. Disorganization, frustrations caused by a host of competing ministries, cavalier treatment of the needed equipment shipped from Germany seemed to be the order of the day. "It is not surprising that Helmut drowns his sorrows in vodka," Frau Gröttrup noted in her diary.

Gröttrup, in an attempt to work out some sort of contractual status for the rocket experts, protested to Colonel General D. F. Ustinov, Minister of Defense Industry:

"How can we be expected to accomplish anything if we have nothing to work with? We have no tools, no equipment —not even tables! One can see the test stands and other materiel brought from Germany sitting there for miles along the railway sidings, rotting and corroding in the snow. Soon it will be nothing but scrap metal."

"Herr Gröttrup," Ustinov replied, "you're not here to complain about what seems to you lack of organization."

"Why am I here, then? I'd like to know!"

"You're in charge of the German Rocket Collective and your job is completing the reconstruction of the A-4. It is proceeding on schedule."

"When will we be allowed to return to Germany?"

Minister of Defense Ustinov laughed at this question and said: "When you can orbit the world in a rocket!"

But slowly, very slowly, the working conditions of the German Rocket Collective improved. Helmut Gröttrup and his associates drove ahead with their work, with the rationalization that they were not so much helping the Russians as the advancement of a great idea; they were, for the most part, apolitical men, interested primarily in rocketry.

Driven by their obsession, they continued with the reconstruction and refinement of V-2. Their wives, however, complained bitterly about the living conditions in Russia and about their husbands' devotion to technical problems. "I can understand the exasperation and hatred of these women," Frau Gröttrup noted in her diary. "Few of them, until now, have had to pass the severe test of living among men who are completely obsessed by their work, men to whom an equation solved means much more than a comfortable bed, who don't care what's put on their plates—like Wernher von Braun, who preferred to eat his potatoes in their skins so he could save himself the time it would take to peel them. One can't really expect good mothers and housewives to understand such fanaticism. . . . Helmut has to take the brunt of it—Helmut, who looks as though he were walking on air whenever something new is discovered."

On August 26, 1947, Irmgard Gröttrup had something more disturbing to cope with than the "gossip and jealousy" among the German wives in the communal mess kitchen attached to the rocket research center in Moscow. She was told by a Soviet minor official that her husband had left Moscow; the official did not know where he had gone nor how long he would be gone.

Frau Gröttrup waited two weeks. When after that time she had received no word from her husband or anyone else as to where he was, she went to the fair-haired, bull-necked Russian manager of the research center where the Germans worked and put the question to him directly.

"Maybe your husband just doesn't like to write letters," the manager observed. "What is your problem? Is the food bad? Don't you have enough money?"

"I want my husband!"

"There are plenty of other men in Russia. Would you like to take a little vacation?"

"I just want my husband back! When is he going to return to Moscow?"

"When his work is finished," the manager said, indicating that the conversation was finished.

For two months Frau Gröttrup kept up a ceaseless badgering of Russian officials to discover the whereabouts of her husband. At last she was informed that she could join him. She was given passage on the night flight from Moscow to the steppes of Kazakhstan, 125 miles east of Stalingrad. She found Helmut Gröttrup in a temporary town of military tents and trucks in an otherwise uninhabited, desert-like area, where she was the only woman. There was a launching pad a few miles away. Helmut Gröttrup had been taken from Mowcow to fire a rocket from the steppes of Kazakhstan. The event was scheduled to take place in a few days. A test stand imported from Germany had already been thrown up by a welding brigade from Stalingrad.

The morning of October 30, 1947, was set for the firing. It dawned cold and clear over the steppes. Neither the Germans brought from Moscow nor the Soviet technicians assigned to observe them had slept the previous night. They were all being observed by high-ranking Soviet military and scientific personages standing in the bunker near the launch pad. The fueling of the rocket lasted two hours. Then the all-clear reports from the tracking stations came in. All instruments and systems were synchronized. The countdown began. "The tension has become so acute that I could scream," Frau Gröttrup noted in her diary. But at zero minus five, or five minutes before the command to fire was to be given, the test stand and the rocket it held slid sideways.

The countdown was canceled. Russian technicians and workmen ran to the test stand, found that one leg of it had given way because of a broken rivet, and proceeded, at great risk, to replace the rivet. Then they winched the stand and the rocket back into correct firing position and propped up the whole with iron girders.

The countdown was resumed. At zero minus one, Helmut Gröttrup gave the command that General Walter Dornberger had always given at Peenemünde: *"Start Freie!"* (Rocket Away!) The first long-range rocket ever fired in the Soviet Union, a V-2 which had been found at Nordhausen and then shipped to Kazakhstan, rose slowly, whipping sand off the area surrounding the launch pad. Then it gathered speed, roared up over the vast steppes, and vanished in the sky. A plane took off for the target area, 185 miles away, and within an hour radioed back that the V-2 had impacted squarely on target.

Helmut Gröttrup was embraced by the Soviet director of the test installation as a turmoil of shouting and rejoicing broke out among the Russian technicians and workmen. The Germans, while they were relieved that the launching had been successful, took the success quietly, as though it had been a matter of course. Some of them wondered if it might mean that they had fulfilled the purpose for which they had been brought to the Soviet Union and would now be permitted to go home.

This first successful test of a V-2 in Russia did not, however, mean that the German Rocket Collective could return to Germany. The Russians were pleased with the test and told Helmut Gröttrup that they were interested in improving the V-2 and increasing its range. Further tests and research would be required.

Three years after the Soviet Secret Police had pounded on the door of the Gröttrups' house in East Germany, Helmut Gröttrup and his wife were still in the Soviet Union. On October 22, 1949, Irmgard Gröttrup noted in her diary: "The great Ustinov himself honored us with a visit. But you can't quiet your conscience with honors, at least a man like Helmut can't. He asked the Minister how much longer we would have to stay in Russia—'Until you and your entire Collective can fly to Berlin by rocket.' I have lost my sense of humor and can only take such cryptic remarks seriously."

The Gröttrups remained in the Soviet Union through 1950. The fact that they were there, along with two hundred other specialists attached to the German Rocket Collective and thousands of other specialists in such areas as jet aircraft and submarines, was well known to the American Central Intelligence Agency, which had been founded in 1947. The fact that Wernher von Braun and the leading members of the old Peenemünde team were engaged in guided missile projects in Texas was, in turn, known by Soviet Intelligence. As early as December 3, 1946, Soviet Intelligence agents could read a press release from the Public Relations Division of the War Department which informed the world for the first time that German and Austrian scientists were working in the United States.

In 1950, however, the fact that there were German scientists working in both the United States and the Soviet Union was treated with only passing interest by the American public. *Overcast* and its Soviet counterpart appeared to be just another mildly interesting story out of World War II. Seven years later, however, the story would prove to have a kicker to it, a delayed punch line that would—literally—echo around the world.

# PART THREE

# AFTERMATH

# 18

# Saturn

On October 4, 1957, a group of space experts attended a conference in Washington in connection with the International Geophysical Year. That evening they went to a party at the Soviet Embassy. One of the scientists was Dr. Richard Porter of General Electric, who twelve years before had interrogated Wernher von Braun at Garmisch-Partenkirchen and led the evacuation of the V-2 personnel from Nordhausen. Since that time, Dr. Porter had been active in the guided missile field and was now chairman of the technical panel responsible for placing an American satellite in orbit during the IGY.

Another guest at the Soviet Embassy was Walter Sullivan, the science reporter for the *New York Times*. During the party, Sullivan was suddenly called to the telephone. His Washington editor told him of a bulletin just received from Moscow. Slowly Sullivan put down the telephone and walked over to Dr. Porter. "It's up," he whispered in Porter's ear.

Sullivan and Porter passed the startling details of the Moscow bulletin to Dr. Lloyd Berkner, head of the United States IGY program. Berkner rapped for quiet on the hors d'oeuvre table. "I wish to make an announcement," he said. "I've just been informed by the *New York Times* that a Russian satellite is in orbit at an elevation of 900 kilometers. I wish to congratulate our Soviet colleagues on their achievement." [1]

The achievement was a metal ball, about twice the size of a basketball, called Sputnik I, the first man-made object to be shot aloft by powerful booster rockets for a successful orbit of the earth. On November 3, 1957, the Russians launched a much heavier satellite, Sputnik II, which carried the dog Laika. It was the first living creature to circle the earth.

The shock waves that spread over America at the commanding Soviet lead in space were tempered by mordant jokes. One of them had the Sputniks greeting each other in German as they passed in outer space. "We captured the wrong Germans!" exclaimed an American general at NATO.

At his first news conference after the launching of Sputnik I, President Eisenhower told the American public that there was a reason for the Soviet lead: "From 1945, when the Russians captured all [sic] the German scientists at Peenemünde, they have centered their attention on the ballistic missile."

The Russians had concentrated on the ballistic missile since 1945, but they had not, of course, captured all of the Peenemünde scientists. The leading men of that organization had been working in the United States since 1945. Nevertheless, some German rocket experts had been taken to the Soviet Union on October 23, 1946, and the suspicion arose that they were chiefly responsible for the astonishing Russian rocket successes.

Nikita Khrushchev responded to these suspicions in a speech at Minsk on January 22, 1958. "We had, indeed, working with us a small group of Germans," Khrushchev said, "who, on termination of their contracts either returned or are now returning to Germany." But, Khrushchev emphasized, these Germans were not responsible for the Sputniks.

They had been developed completely by Soviet scientists. Grinning, Khrushchev asked his Minsk audience: "If Germans helped Russians, why don't Germans help the United States? After all, American troops seized the chief designer of the V-2, took him to America, and he now builds rockets out there." [2] (Laughter, applause, stamping of feet.)

What had really happened? In this case, Khrushchev was telling the truth, and the truth was more disturbing than the persistent legend that captured German scientists had developed the big booster rockets which had launched the Sputniks and which were obviously also capable of carrying nuclear warheads from the Soviet Union to all points in Europe and to the United States itself.

The Russians had followed a careful plan with the German Rocket Collective. It was pumped dry of its knowledge of V-2 and then put through a lengthy cooling-off period while the Russians carried out their own research and testing, of which they told the captured Germans nothing. Beginning in March 1951, the German rocket experts got their oft-expressed wish to be shipped home. Some of them stayed in East Germany, and others went on to West Germany, where they were picked up and interrogated in depth by the Central Intelligence Agency. Soviet Intelligence made no great effort to prevent these defections because it knew that the C.I.A. would learn next to nothing from the returned Germans about the real nature of the Soviet thrust in rocketry.

Helmut Gröttrup, for example, had seen his responsibilities and generous salary gradually diminish after that first great morning on the Kazakhstan plain in 1947 when the first long-range rocket ever fired in Russia, a V-2, had been launched. In December 1950, Gröttrup was relieved of his post as chief of the German Rocket Collective, and on March 3, 1951, Irmgard Gröttrup noted in her diary: "The German Collective is now a fiction. Our men get their work given them by the Russians who question each of them about the work they did before. . . ." And on February 17, 1952, Frau Gröttrup wrote: "Our men are leading a pleasant enough life at the Institute, but the [Russian] engineers who have been transferred here seem to regard them rather as museum pieces. . . . Helmut's salary, reduced by more than half, is now ridiculously small. . . ."

On November 15, 1953, Helmut Gröttrup was told that he and his family could go home. His last assignment in the Soviet Union had had nothing to do with rocketry; it was the development of an electronic computer. The Gröttrups arrived in East Germany on December 28, 1953, and from there went on to West Germany, where they are living today. The plain truth of the matter was that they had been released because the Russians no longer needed them or the assistance of any other foreign scientists.

The plain truth, however, had some subtle shadings not mentioned by Khrushchev in his speech at Minsk. The Russians, who had no long-range rockets in 1945, could not have developed them as quickly as they did without the initial help provided by the V-2 spoils of war. The Soviet achievement would have taken place, but at a much later date had it not been for the building block of the Nordhausen *Mittelwerke*, the copies of the rocket plans which were found there, and the early tutelage of Helmut Gröttrup and the other Peenemünde men who had been shipped to the Soviet Union by the Secret Police. The truth also was that the Soviet Union would not have been first in space if the story of the men brought to the United States in 1945 under *Overcast* had followed a different course, if the world's wealthiest and most technically capable nation had used its find to drive ahead with a missile and space program with the same concentrated determination it had displayed in the atom bomb project.

In October 1946, the short-term contracts of the von Braun team at Fort Bliss had been extended for five years.

In December 1946, the families of the rocket men began to arrive at Fort Bliss from Germany. In 1948, the surveillance and restrictions on the movement of the Germans at Fort Bliss were relaxed. Classified material was increasingly made available to them, and they were permitted to apply for visas as resident aliens, which opened the way for future American citizenship.

By 1950, Army Ordnance needed a permanent research and development center on a larger scale than Fort Bliss for its expanding military rocket program. Largely through the efforts of Colonel Toftoy, a suitable complex was secured at Huntsville, in northern Alabama. This was a combination of the old Huntsville Arsenal, which had been a Chemical Corps installation in World War II, and the nearby Redstone Arsenal, which had produced artillery shells during World War II. Accompanied by Lieutenant Colonel James Hamill, von Braun and his team arrived in Huntsville on April 1, 1950, and shortly thereafter were given their first big original missile assignment in the United States—the development of the Redstone, a surface-to-surface missile with a two-hundred-mile range to be deployed in the support of ground troops.

On August 20, 1953, the Redstone was successfully launched from Cape Canaveral. It was a military rocket, but von Braun, who was now Chief, Guided Missiles Development Division, Ordnance Missile Laboratory, had not forgotten his long-standing dream of using rocket propulsion for space exploration. In September 1953, he presented a detailed plan to Army and Navy officials for orbiting an American earth satellite using the Redstone as a booster rocket. By the following August, the Army and Navy had decided to cooperate in moving ahead with this project, which was given the name Orbiter. Von Braun and the men working with him were confident that they could launch an American satellite in Project Orbiter by the middle of 1956.

On April 15, 1955, von Braun and most of the members of

his team became American citizens in a ceremony conducted at the Huntsville High School auditorium. They had also begun to develop an intermediate-range ballistic missile for the Army called Jupiter, with a range of fifteen hundred miles. These advances were followed by a crushing disappointment. On July 29, 1955, the White House announced that President Eisenhower had given his approval to the launching of an earth-circling scientific satellite as part of United States participation in the International Geophysical Year, which was to begin in July 1957. The Redstone, however, would not be the rocket used to boost the satellite into orbit. An entirely new, nonmilitary rocket, the Vanguard, would be built for this purpose by the Naval Research Laboratory under the guidance of the National Academy of Sciences. The next day, July 30, the Soviet Union announced that it also planned to launch an earth satellite during the International Geophysical Year.

Von Braun and his Army team, however, did not abandon their objective of space exploration with the shelving of Project Orbiter. In May 1956, the Army requested that the Jupiter rocket be considered as an alternative to the untried Vanguard if the latter should encounter difficulties in development. The request was refused by the Department of Defense. In November 1956, von Braun and his missile team received another blow. Secretary of Defense Charles Wilson issued an edict fixing the areas of jurisdiction of the Army, Navy, and Air Force in developing missiles of various ranges. The Air Force was given jurisdiction over all long-range missiles, while the Army was restricted to missiles having a range of not more than two hundred miles. This meant that von Braun and his group, who worked for the Army, were officially restricted from developing missiles powerful enough to be used for space exploration.

After the launchings of the first two Sputniks, the world waited to see whether the United States, now well behind in the space race, would succeed in orbiting a satellite. On

December 6, 1957, a Vanguard rocket was readied for this purpose at Cape Canaveral. It was fired, rose a few feet, then fell back on its launch pad in flames, a dismal failure.

Then, on January 31, 1958, at 8:30 P.M., the countdown started at Cape Canaveral for another American booster rocket, the Jupiter-C. The Department of Defense had reconsidered its decision and authorized von Braun and his associates at the Army Ballistic Missile Agency to attempt a satellite shot. In the nose of the Jupiter-C was Explorer I, a small satellite developed by the Jet Propulsion Laboratory of the California Institute of Technology. At 10:48 P.M. the Jupiter-C was fired from its launch pad by Dr. Kurt Debus, who had been in charge of rocket launchings at Peenemünde. It worked perfectly and placed Explorer I into orbit. In March 1958, von Braun and his team fired Explorer III and, in July 1958, Explorer IV. The Army team went on to other successes, but von Braun, despite the adulation and publicity which suddenly descended upon him, remained realistic. "Our little Explorers . . . are competing with the *Sputniks* in spirit only," he said. "But in terms of rocket hardware they are no match." And they were not. The later flights of the Soviet cosmonauts, always more spectacular and ahead of those of the American astronauts, only confirmed the fact that the Russians had a commanding lead in booster rockets capable of hurling huge payloads into space.

By July 1958, the attempt to overtake the Soviet lead in space had become a priority undertaking for the United States Government. Space exploration was taken out of the hands of the military services and made the responsibility of a new civilian agency, the heavily staffed and financed National Aeronautics and Space Administration. On July 1, 1960, Wernher von Braun and his associates were transferred from the Army Ballistic Missile Agency to NASA. Part of the Redstone Arsenal became the George C. Marshall Space Flight Center, with von Braun as its civilian director. After having worked on military missiles ever since Walter Dornberger had hired him in 1932 for the infant German rocket program, von Braun no longer had to concern himself with them. His new assignment was simply stated in a brochure distributed on September 8, 1960, at the dedication ceremonies of the Marshall Space Flight Center at Huntsville which were attended by, among others, President Eisenhower, Mrs. Marshall, Governor Patterson of Alabama, Mayor R. B. "Specs" Searcy of Huntsville, and Major General Holger Toftoy, U.S.A. (Ret.).

> The current major mission is to develop an efficient and reliable system for lifting multi-ton loads into orbit around the earth and into deep space. The vehicle under development for this purpose is the Saturn which will ultimately be capable of transporting men around the moon and back to earth, or placing instruments on Mars or Venus.

On May 25, 1961, a new President, John F. Kennedy, in a speech to Congress, went one step further in defining American objectives in space: "I believe that this nation should commit itself to achieving the goal, before this decade is out, of landing a man on the moon and returning him safely to earth." To this enterprise the name Project Apollo was given.

Apollo involves hundreds of interrelated organizations in government and private industry and over a hundred thousand people with skills in almost every known science. Wernher von Braun and his rocket team at the Marshall Space Flight Center are no longer, as they were at Fort Bliss, Texas, in 1945, the only experienced space experts in the United States. And yet the success of Project Apollo, especially in reaching the moon before the Soviet Union can accomplish that objective, depends on the development of the Saturn rocket at Huntsville, Alabama.

The early Soviet successes in space were due to the tremendous thrust power of their rockets, which could launch bigger manned capsules on flights of much longer duration than any attempted by the United States. But the Soviet rockets, as of the summer of 1964, were still not powerful enough to hurl a manned capsule to the moon. For this, an entirely new and giant rocket must be designed, both by the Soviet Union and the United States. The American rocket is the Saturn. Advanced versions of it will have a take-off weight of three thousand tons, equal to that of a light cruiser.

The Marshall Space Flight Center has the money and the talent to develop the Saturn. Its annual payroll of fifty-five million dollars accounts for over six thousand people. Only eighty-nine of them are former Peenemünde men, for many of the group that came to Texas in 1945 under *Overcast* left government service for better-paying jobs in private industry. Von Braun, however, was able to hold the oldest team of rocket experts in the world together to a remarkable degree, and they form the core of the vast Marshall organization.*

By 1964, some objections had been voiced to an inflexible deadline for sending Americans to the moon by 1970 and spending some forty billion dollars to engage in a race to the moon with the Soviet Union. Doubts were voiced that such a race was actually in progress. Soviet plans for a lunar voyage, however, remain—as have all Russian space efforts —cloaked in secrecy.

Von Braun and the other members of the old Peenemünde team at Huntsville have little doubt that an advanced Saturn

* Dr. Eberhard Rees is von Braun's deputy director for research and development, and the other R & D divisions are headed by members of the old team: Aeroballistics, Dr. E. D. Geissler; Computation, Dr. Helmut Hoelzer; Manufacturing Engineering, Werner Kuers; Astrionics, Dr. Walter Hauessermann; Research Projects, Dr. Ernst Stuhlinger; Propulsion and Vehicle Engineering, W. A. Mrazek; Quality Assurance, Dieter Grau; Test, Karl Heimberg. Directors of staff and project offices are Dr. O. H. Lange, Saturn Systems; Dr. Hans Hueter, Light and Medium Vehicles; Hans Maus, Central Planning; and H. H. Koelle, Future Projects. Dr. Kurt Debus is now in charge of the Launch Operations Directorate at Cape Kennedy and reports directly to NASA headquarters in Washington.

will be ready to send Americans to the moon by 1970. The Saturn test flights have been stunningly successful. On January 29, 1964, a Saturn I roared skyward on a river of flame at Cape Kennedy and placed into orbit its ten-ton payload, the heaviest space craft payload in history. An editorial in the *New York Times* commented: "The successful flight of Saturn I yesterday opens a new era in United States exploration of space. In less than six years the amount of weight the United States can put into orbit at one time has multiplied roughly a thousand-fold. The object that Saturn I sent circling the heavens is heavier than any Soviet Sputnik launched to date."

On May 28th, 1964, and again on September 18, a Saturn placed an 8.5-ton unmanned test model of the Apollo lunar spacecraft, developed by the Manned Spacecraft Center in Houston, Texas, into low earth orbit. The next major step is to lift three men into orbit aboard an Apollo capsule sometime in 1966 to practice for the moon journey.

To hear the unearthly, basso roar of Saturn echoing from its static test gantry through the streets of Huntsville and over the nearby cotton fields and forests of loblolly pine is to believe that the moon is no longer a quarter of a million miles away, but in practical terms sixty hours from earth. The George C. Marshall Space Flight Center is a busy place, too much concerned with the future to give any thought to the past. Indeed, only two things in the Alabama city of Huntsville give any reminder of how Saturn and the age of guided missiles and space exploration began. The Space Flight Center is sometimes referred to by local wags as Peenemünde South. And set up in a row before the Space Museum like fantastic arrows pointed at the stars is a display of "hardware" developed by von Braun and his team. At the beginning of the row, resurrected out of a junkyard, stands the grandfather of all the big rockets used today, both in the United States and the Soviet Union. It is a V-2.

# APPENDIX: Some questions and facts about Overcast / Paperclip

The secret War Department General Staff project for importing German and Austrian scientists and engineers to the United States after World War II was, of course, not the first instance of American utilization of European scientific talent. In an informal way, this had begun much earlier than the summer of 1945.

In the first three decades of this century, Germany possessed a scientific establishment that was probably unmatched anywhere in the world. To a great degree, it was destroyed, never to regain its former eminence, after Hitler and the Nazis came to power in 1933. It has been estimated that between 1933 and 1939, because of Nazi political and racial practices, Germany lost the services of one-half of her physicists and two-thirds of her physical chemists. Many of these men, along with their colleagues from other European countries, emigrated to the United States. To grasp the significance of this foreign-aid program unwittingly instigated by the Nazis, one has only to recall the contributions made to the development of the atom bomb by Einstein; Enrico Fermi, an Italian; and the Hungarians, Leo Szilard and Edward Teller.

A formidable body of scientific talent remained in the

Third Reich, however, through World War II. Hitler and his chief aides, while not interested in pure science, were interested in science when it could be applied to immediate military applications such as jet aircraft, new types of submarines, and rockets. The Nazis, hoping they could narrow the gap between the conventional armed forces available to the Third Reich and the Allies, made huge sums of money available for developing such weapons, but none of them became operational until after the defeat of the Third Reich was assured.

The reason for this failure is now obvious. The Nazi state, which appeared monolithic and efficient to foreign observers in the early years of World War II, was in reality an inefficient mosaic of competing ministries, petty bureaucrats, racial and political "philosophers," rival military organizations, and secret police, all of whose activities had the end result of impeding the work of the scientists of the Third Reich. The scientists themselves do not appear to have been avid supporters of Hitler. Dr. Samuel Goudsmit, the Dutch-born leader of the American Alsos mission which was charged with determining how far the Germans had progressed with atom bomb development, later wrote: "On the whole, we gained the definite impression that German scientists did not support their country in the war effort. The principal thing was to obtain money from the government for their own researches, pretending that they might be of value to the war effort."

Whatever the attitude of most of the German scientists toward the Nazis might have been, the British and American governments realized that something would have to be done about them when the Third Reich surrendered. They would have to be located and interrogated for their priceless information. More importantly, they would have to be prevented from being used as a nucleus for future German military resurgence. It had become evident with the appearance of the jet plane, the atom bomb, and the long-range guided missile that the nature of warfare had changed. Future wars would be decided not by the generals and the traditional land and naval forces but by the scientist.

In the fall of 1944, when the defeat of the Third Reich became a certainty, the British and American governments began to plan for the administration of postwar Germany. These deliberations resulted in the *Eclipse* plan, which took into account the *Safehaven* project worked out earlier by the U. S. State Department. *Safehaven* specifically concerned itself with "the control of German individuals who might contribute to the revival of the German war potential by subversive activities in foreign countries after the war." The Alsos mission also found the time apart from its atom bomb investigations to analyze the threat to world security posed by the existence of a large group of talented German scientists and the problems involved in controlling these civilians in occupied postwar Germany.

The *Eclipse, Safehaven* and Alsos findings had not gotten beyond the discussion stage, however, when the Third Reich suddenly began to collapse in the spring of 1945. In early May 1945, Supreme Headquarters, Allied Expeditionary Forces, was obliged to cable the Policy Staff of the War Department General Staff for instructions to guide it in controlling scientific research in Germany. Investigators from the Army Ground and Air Forces and the Navy were active in Germany, but their missions were limited to on-the-spot interrogations. There was no overall policy for actually bringing German scientists to the United States, and no policy for their future control. There was no "Operation Paperclip," but simply a group of frequently competitive technical teams from the American armed forces attempting to locate, and then to interrogate on the spot, German scientists.

Some American officers, however, came to realize that short interrogations in Germany itself could not fully exploit the knowledge of the German scientists. Documentation appears to indicate that Major General Hugh J. Knerr, Deputy Commanding General for Administration of the U.S. Strategic Air Forces in Europe, was the first American to recommend that selected German scientists be brought to the United States. He advocated this to Robert A. Lovett, Assistant Secretary of War for Air, during the latter's tour of the European Theater in early April 1945. Knerr was thinking of specialists who could aid in the development of jet engines at Wright Field, Ohio.

On May 22, a cable (written by Major Robert Staver and signed by Colonel Joel Holmes) went to the Pentagon from Paris Ordnance Headquarters recommending that one hundred of the Peenemünde rocket specialists be evacuated to the United States. By this time, committees within the War and State Departments were already at work on the details of a plan (still unnamed) for bringing German scientists to the United States. In fact, a small group of them was already in America. Members of the Navy Technical Mission in Europe had interrogated Professor Herbert Wagner of Henschel Aircraft in April 1945 and decided that his knowledge of the Hs 2T3, a radio-controlled air-to-air missile, could be fully exploited only in the United States. On May 4, 1945, the Director of Naval Intelligence had requested his immediate evacuation from Europe without waiting for a formal policy statement. On May 19, 1945, Wagner and four of his assistants, whose "knowledge, experience, and skills" were said to be "unmatched anywhere in the world," arrived in Washington. After four weeks of interrogation at a Washington hotel, they were transferred to an estate at Sands Point, Long Island, to work on a Navy missile undertaking called Project 77. This was the beginning of what would later be a wholesale importation of German scientists.

By May 21, 1945, many of the preliminary details for *Overcast* had been settled. On that date, Major L. F. Cranford,

Chief, Interrogation Branch, Office of the Assistant Chief of Air Staff, Intelligence, sent a memorandum to the Assistant Chief of Air Staff, Intelligence:

SUBJECT: German Civilian Technicians

1. The Assistant Chief of Staff, G-2, WDGS [Military Intelligence, War Department General Staff], has charged Captured Personnel and Materiel Branch MIS [Military Intelligence Service] with the responsibility of immediately implementing and setting up an organization which will cover the handling of subject personnel re: requisition and transportation from ETO to Zone of Interior [the United States] quarters and subsistence, pay, security and all other pertinent details.

2. As soon as all details have been cleared with State Department, Justice Department, and other interested agencies subject personnel upon request will be brought to a "central pool" for interrogation and exploitation of the AAF, AGF, and ASF [Army Air, Ground, and Service Forces]. Subject personnel may also be moved to other parts of the Zone of the Interior for further exploitation.

3. Subject personnel will not be handled as prisoners of war.

It was not until July 19, 1945, that all of the details were cleared through the departments of State, Justice, Commerce, and Labor, the Office of Scientific Research and Development, and other government agencies, and the plan assigned the code name of *Overcast*.

*Overcast* was very definitely a short-term project. Interested military agencies would submit to Major General Clayton Bissell, Assistant Chief of Staff for Military Intelligence of the War Department General Staff, "through channels, lists of names of specialists desired for exploitation in the United States." Military Intelligence would bring the men requested to the United States and turn them over to the agencies which had requested them. Three hundred and fifty specialists could be requested by all of the services under the

War Department (Army Air, Ground, and Service Forces), and the Navy Department, which participated in the project. The 350 specialists would be offered contracts for six months, renewable for another six months, as most of them were. After a year of what was termed "exploitation," they would be returned to Germany by Military Intelligence. No provision was made for bringing the families of the scientists to the United States.

The official purpose of *Overcast* was to utilize the expertise of the scientists selected in developing weapons that could be helpful in "shortening the Japanese war." On July 19, 1945, few of the officials who had formulated *Overcast* knew about the atom bomb and that it would bring a quick end to the Japanese war. When V-J day came on September 2, 1945, 350 German scientists had been selected for *Overcast* and steps had been taken to bring them to the United States for a purpose that no longer existed. Unofficially, however, *Overcast* had two other purposes that were never put on record but were clearly understood by the officials connected with the project. One was to prevent the Germans from falling into the hands of the Russians, and the other was to prevent them from being used for a revival of German military power.

*Overcast*, then, was a short-term, overall War Department project. It was not solely or specifically concerned with bringing the German rocket experts to Fort Bliss, Texas, although they later became the most famous of the German specialists who were imported.


WHAT WAS OPERATION PAPERCLIP?

To the author's knowledge, every book, newspaper, and magazine article that has referred to the location of scientists in Germany in the spring of 1945 and their subsequent evacuation to the United States has labeled this enterprise "Operation Papcrclip." This, of course, is a mistake, but an understandable one. As noted in Chapter 16, there was a Project Paperclip, but it was simply an extension of the original *Overcast* project. The former German Army cavalry barracks at Landshut, Bavaria, where the families of the scientists were housed by the U. S. Army while the men were working on their one-year contracts in the United States eventually picked up the nickname "Camp Overcast" for reasons never determined. Fearing that this might create a security problem, the War Department simply assigned another code word to *Overcast*. On March 13, 1946, the secretary of the Joint Chiefs of Staff sent out this memorandum to interested agencies:

SUBJECT: Substitution of Code Word
  1. Effective this date, the code word PAPERCLIP has been substituted for the code word OVERCAST, due to the compromise of the latter word.
  2. The meaning previously attached to OVERCAST was not compromised and will now attach to PAPERCLIP.

Under the name of *Paperclip,* and as a result of the prodding of the various armed services which came to realize the value of the German scientists and did not want to release them after one year, a revision of the original short-term exploitation plan was coordinated by the War Department General Staff. It was approved by the Secretary of War on July 31, 1946, and forwarded to the State-War-Navy Coordinating Committee, which worked out a policy that was recommended by the State Department to the President. Harry Truman signed his approval on September 3, 1946.

The revised *Paperclip* projcct opencd the door to longrange exploitation and the eventual achievement of immigrant status by the Germans, authorized bringing their dependents to the United States (the first ones arrived in December 1946), and raised the number of scientists who could be recruited from 350 to 1,000. By the spring of 1948, *Paperclip* had grown to an operation of sizable proportions. As of May 18, 1948, there were 1,136 German and Austrian nationals in the United States. Four hundred and ninety-two were specialists, and 644 were their dependents. Of the specialists, 177 were employed by the Army, 205 by the Air Force, 72 by the Navy, and 38 by the Department of Commerce.

The largest single group did not consist of the rocket men at Fort Bliss, who numbered 127 men by the spring of 1948, but 146 specialists employed by the Air Force at Wright Field, Ohio. There was, however, an important difference. The rocket group was a cohesive, integrated team that had worked together for years, while the other *Paperclip* scientists were gifted individuals whose talents were not concentrated on a specific objective.

The recruitment of German scientists for work in the United States did not stop until early 1950, when the Bonn government was successful in persuading the United States government to cease this drain on one of West Germany's natural resources.

## WAS THERE OPPOSITION TO OVERCAST AND PAPERCLIP?

The American public and the legislative branches of the U. S. government had no opportunity to express their approval or disapproval of the original *Overcast* project. The War Department, with State Department approval, simply brought the German scientists into the United States and put them to work without officially announcing or acknowledging that they were here until December 3, 1946.

Although at this late date there seems to be little point in employing the wisdom of hindsight to criticize certain individuals for their actions in the immediate postwar era, when feeling against anything of German origin was high, there is evidence to indicate that many American military officers, government officials, and scientists were not favorably disposed to the importation of German scientists, whether they had been nominal Nazi party members or not. But one can give credit to the foresight of such men as Colonel Gervais Trichel and Colonel Holger Toftoy for grasping the long-term benefits that would accrue to the United States through the employment of the German rocket specialists and for energetically pressing for that employment through the paper battles of numerous Pentagon committees in 1945.

When on December 3, 1946, the Press Section, Public Relations Division of the War Department, issued a release announcing for the first time that the German and Austrian scientists were working in the United States, a considerable amount of criticism ensued.

On December 30, 1946, a group of eminent individuals, including Albert Einstein, Richard Neuberger, Philip Murray, Rabbi Stephen Wise, and Norman Vincent Peale, sent this collective telegram to President Truman:

> We hold these individuals to be potentially dangerous carriers of racial and religious hatred. Their former eminence as Nazi party members and supporters raises the issue of their fitness to become American citizens and hold key positions in American industrial, scientific, and educational institutions. If it is deemed imperative to utilize these individuals in this country we earnestly petition you to make sure that they will not be granted permanent residence or citizenship in the United States with the opportunity which that could afford of inculcating those anti-democratic doctrines which seek to undermine and destroy our national unity.

The Commission of Law and Social Action of the American Jewish Congress made a detailed study of *Paperclip* and presented it to Senator Homer Ferguson in an attempt to gain his support for a congressional investigation. Representative John Dingell (D. Mich.) told the House of Representatives that "he had never thought we were so poor mentally . . . to have to import for the defense of our country." On January 22, 1946, Dr. Vannevar Bush, Director of the Office of Scientific Research and Development, wrote to President Truman that in his opinion the *Paperclip* undertaking was "decidedly unwise."

On March 24, 1947, W. A. Higenbotham, executive secretary of the Federation of American Scientists, an organization claiming three thousand members, wrote to President Truman recommending that German scientists brought to the United States for work on military research projects be denied jobs in private industry or education. "Any favor extended to such individuals," Higenbotham wrote, "even for military reasons, represents an affront to the people of all countries who so recently fought beside us, to the refugees whose lives were shattered by Nazism, to our unfortunate scientific colleagues of formerly occupied lands, and to all those others who suffered under the yoke these men helped to forge."

Protests such as these, however, diminished with the onset of the cold war and gradually ceased altogether. By August 1949, the postwar hostility had changed to such a degree that Wernher von Braun could be made an honorary fellow of the British Interplanetary Society, "in recognition of your great pioneering activities in the field of rocket engineering."

## WHAT DID THE UNITED STATES GET OUT OF OVERCAST AND PAPERCLIP?

It is worth noting that the German scientists imported under *Overcast* were paid, while they still worked for the armed services, modest civil service salaries in no case exceeding ten thousand dollars a year, plus being given quarters that can only be described as modest. None of them has ever been involved in any breach of security or a case of subversion or espionage. In recruiting them, the United States denied their expertise to the Soviet Union and also reaped benefits that were considerable.

This writer has not been able to discover what tangible results may have been yielded by the employment of one *Paperclip* man at the Bureau of Mines at Grand Forks, North Dakota, or two at the Food and Container Institute of the Armed Forces in Chicago. But, leaving aside the men who worked on Air Force and Navy projects, the contributions made to the United States by the former Peenemünde rocket specialists can be ascertained. This group, always working with representatives from American industry, government, and the universities, was largely responsible for a number of purely military missile developments for Army Ordnance. These include:

a) The first American penetration of outer space. On February 29, 1949, at White Sands, a V-2 boosted a two-stage WAC Corporal rocket to an altitude of 259 miles, a record which stood for eight years.

b) The first successful launching of an intermediate-range ballistic missile, the 1,500-mile Jupiter, in May 1957.

When the former Peenemünde group working with Army Ordnance switched to space projects, it produced:

a) The first American satellite of the earth, Explorer I, boosted into orbit by a Jupiter-C rocket on January 31, 1958.

b) The first American satellite of the sun, Pioneer IV, March 2, 1959.

c) The first American flight into space by living creatures, the monkeys Able and Baker, and their successful recovery, May 28, 1959.

d) The first American astronaut, Alan Shepard, was boosted into suborbital flight by an Army Redstone rocket on May 5, 1961, a flight repeated by Virgil Grissom on July 21, 1961.

John Glenn, the first American to orbit the earth, circled the globe three times in a Mercury spacecraft launched February 20, 1962, by the model D version of the Atlas. This rocket was not developed by the von Braun team but was a modified intercontinental ballistic missile developed by the Air Force. The Atlas, however, while adequate for launching the Project Mercury astronauts, is not powerful enough to serve as the launch vehicle for the Project Apollo moon journey.

Since being transferred to civilian National Aeronautics and Space Administration on July 1, 1960, von Braun and his team have developed Saturn C-1, which has a thrust in excess of a million pounds. Saturn was successfully test-fired on October 27, 1961, and has had six further successful test firings from Cape Kennedy. It is believed to be the most powerful booster rocket now in existence anywhere, including the Soviet Union. The planned advanced versions of the Saturn will have engines capable of generating 7,500,000 pounds of thrust at launch, twenty times more powerful than the Atlas. The hangar building for the advanced Saturn will be bigger than the Pentagon and almost as high as the Washington Monument; the launch complex required for the moon trip will be a Florida island encompassing 80,000 acres, six times the size of Manhatten Island. The first test flight of the monster rocket is scheduled for 1966.

## WAS THE LONG-RANGE GUIDED MISSILE INVENTED AT PEENEMÜNDE?

Von Braun would be the last person to claim that he and his team invented the long-range guided missile or developed the basic theories and mathematics of rocket propulsion. Such developments are necessarily international in concept, the result of the pioneering work of many men in many lands. To give only one example, Dr. Robert Goddard of Worcester, Massachusetts, had as far back as 1914 been granted patents on the multi-stage rocket and the liquid-fueled rocket engine, two concepts that were later to provide the fundamental building blocks for space exploration. On March 16, 1926, at Auburn, Massachusetts, Goddard launched the world's first successful liquid-fueled rocket; it rose forty-one feet in the air. Had Dr. Goddard, who died in 1944, been given the necessary research funds by American military and government officials in the 1930's, it is probable that the United States would have had a long-range guided missile before V-2 was put into action. As it was, despite Goddard's pioneering work, none of his rockets attained more than a few thousand feet altitude. (An interesting full-length biography of Dr. Goddard, *This High Man,* by Milton Lehman, was published in October 1963.)

What happened at Peenemünde was that von Braun and his associates were provided with the men, materials, and money to put their imaginations and engineering excellence to work in turning existing theories and primitive experiments into practical application. The result was V-2, the world's first long-range guided missile, of which all the big rockets of today are refined and improved extensions.

## WHAT HAPPENED TO THE MEN INVOLVED IN OVERCAST?

As noted in Chapter 18, von Braun, as director of the George C. Marshall Space Flight Center, has succeeded in keeping eighty-nine of the former Peenemünde men with him as an integrated team. They are the oldest team of rocket experts in the world, with experience in the field spanning three decades. Some members of the original group of 127 at Fort Bliss, Texas, later went into private industry upon achieving resident alien status and then citizenship.

Bernhard Tessmann, who hid the V-2 documents in the Dörnten mine, is still with von Braun at the Marshall Space Flight Center. But Dieter Huzel, for example, the man who helped Tessmann hide the documents, is now with North American Aviation's Space and Information Systems Division in California. Dr. Martin Schilling is vice-president in charge of engineering and research of the Raytheon Company; von Braun's younger brother, Magnus, is with the Missile Division of the Chrysler Corporation; Dr. Theodore Buchold with General Electric; Krafft Ehricke with the Convair Astronautics Division of General Dynamics; Dr. Ernst Steinhoff with the RAND Corporation; Walther Riedel returned to West Germany and a job in private industry there, and so on. Nevertheless, the von Braun team at Huntsville, Alabama, is basically the same one that formed the heart of the Peenemünde organization.

As noted in Chapters Fifteen and Sixteen, Major General Walter Dornberger did not come to the United States until July 1947, and then did not rejoin his old Peenemünde team at Fort Bliss but instead went to work for the Air Force as a guided missile consultant. In May 1950, Dr. Dornberger joined Bell Aircraft. As of June 1964, he was vice-president and chief scientist of Bell Aerosystems Company, a division of Bell Aerospace Corporation, Buffalo. Still vigorous in his late sixties, Dr. Dornberger has been involved in a number of important space projects, such as the Bell X-1, the world's first rocket airplane, and the rocket-boosted, hypersonic glider Dyna-Soar. He is an ardent advocate of manned spacecraft that can be maneuvered in space and then brought back to a predetermined landing strip.

The Americans who were involved in *Overcast* in the spring of 1945 had, by 1964, all gone their separate ways from the von Braun team. Robert Staver left the Army in December 1945 with the rank of lieutenant colonel in the Reserve and now lives in Los Altos, California, near his alma mater, Stanford, where he is engaged in private business having nothing to do with rockets. Dr. Richard Porter lives in Connecticut and remains with the General Electric Company. He was elected president of the American Rocket Society in 1955 and is now the president of the International Committee on Space Research (COSPAR). Joel G. Holmes retired from the Regular Army with the permanent rank of brigadier general and is now an executive with Mason & Hanger-Silas Mason Co., Inc., an engineering and contracting firm in Burlington, Iowa. Colonel Gervais Trichel retired from the Regular Army in 1947, later became manager of the European office of the Chrysler Corporation Defense Operations Division, and is now an executive with Chrysler in Detroit. James Hamill served as Chief of the Ordnance Guided Missile Center at Huntsville, Alabama, and retired in 1961 from his last post as a colonel in charge of Ballistic Research Laboratory at the Aberdeen Proving Ground. He lives in Washington, D. C., and is with the American Ordnance Association.

Holger Toftoy is probably the man who knows von Braun and the old Peenemünde men better than anyone else in the United States. From August 1945, when he arrived at the schoolhouse in Witzenhausen, Germany, as Chief of the Army Ordnance Rocket Branch with the authorization to select one hundred German rocket specialists for work in the United States, until 1958, when he was transferred from his post as commanding general of Redstone Arsenal, Toftoy acted not only as the leader but as the friend and confidant of the German group, which went through some trying periods of frustration and discouragement. Toftoy has become known as "Mr. Missile," and part of the citation for the Distinguished Service Medal which was awarded to him explains why—"responsible for major initial decisions and follow-up on the development of a number of post war rocket weapons, including the super bazooka and the large HONEST JOHN. Atomic fire support by mobile rockets such as HONEST JOHN originated and reached fruition under his supervision. Through his efforts the NIKE and CORPORAL guided missile systems were developed. His insight and management have contributed substantially to the development of Army missiles such as NIKE AJAX, NIKE HERCULES and HAWK which today are counted on to provide much of the air defense capability of North America. He secured appropriate technical objectives and necessary resources for the early developmental stages of REDSTONE far ahead of present widespread recognition of the military value of ballistic missiles. It was a modified version of the REDSTONE, the JUPITER C, that successfully launched the 'EXPLORER,' the free world's first earth satellite. . . ."

The citizens of Huntsville, Alabama, erected a monument to Toftoy in Big Spring Park upon his departure from Redstone Arsenal in 1958 to become commanding general of the Aberdeen Proving Ground. Probably no civic monument has been better deserved. Toftoy was responsible to a large degree for bringing the Army rocket research and development operation, and the German experts, to Huntsville in 1950 from Fort Bliss. Huntsville at the time was a somewhat somnolent cotton-mill community of 16,000 souls, styled by its Chamber of Commerce "The Water Cress Capital of the World." By 1964, Huntsville had a growing population of 90,000 and called itself "Rocket City, U.S.A." After thirty-six years of service, Toftoy retired from the Army as a major general in command of the Aberdeen Proving Ground in 1958. He now lives in Treasure Island, Florida, and serves as a missile consultant to Northrop and other firms.

## WHO DID WHAT?

This book has related the story of *Crossbow, Overcast,* and *Paperclip* through the experiences of some of the key men who developed V-2 and the Americans who played major roles in bringing them to the United States. But just as the Apollo moon project is not the responsibility of one man or one group of men, neither was an undertaking of the size and scope of *Overcast.* From Cordell Hull, Secretary of State in 1945, to the tankers of the 3rd Armored Division who took Nordhausen, hundreds of men were involved in one way or another in *Overcast.* For those who are partial to having their stories neatly wrapped up, with kudos awarded to single individuals for having alone conceived and executed such operations as *Overcast,* this writer can only quote from a letter he received from Gervais Trichel in November 1962:

> Personally I feel that the contributions of Wernher von Braun and the German scientific group have been of tremendous significance to the American effort in long-range rocket development with missile and space applications. Many people had a part in the Project of securing their services and entry into the United States. To me, it seems of little

consequence who did what, the important thing is they did reach the United States and have achieved notable successes in their undertakings. This has been of benefit not only to all Americans, but to the Free World.

# ACKNOWLEDGEMENTS

In attempting to tell for the first time in pattern and detail the story of *Crossbow* and *Overcast* as it related to V-2, I have drawn upon my own experiences as an intelligence officer for a U.S. government agency in postwar Germany, but to a much greater degree on background material supplied by a sizable number of individuals and organizations. For documentary material I am principally indebted to Lieutenant Colonel Gene Guerney, Director of the United States Air Force Book Program and Mr. Albert Simpson, Chief, USAF Historical Division, who, from the archives of the Research Studies Institute of the Air University at Maxwell Air Force Base, Alabama, made available to me key documents that had previously been classified.

Mr. William Peifer, an historian attached to the staff of the Office of the Chief of Military History, the Pentagon, provided good counsel and helpful leads, as did Mr. L. A. Jackets, Head of Air Historical Branch, British Air Ministry. The Office of Information, Department of the Army, and especially Mr. Bart Slattery, Director of Information, the George C. Marshall Space Flight Center, and Joe Jones of his office, were of great assistance in providing leads and background information. Mr. Richard Gibbs and Mrs. Donald K. Garber helped with research. Brigadier General Joel G. Holmes, U.S.A. (Ret.), and Colonel Gervais Trichel, U.S.A. (Ret.), threw light on some controversial points in correspondence. This book could not have been written without the assistance of the people who play the major roles in it: Dr. Richard Porter, Major General Holger N. Toftoy, U.S.A.

(Ret.), Dr. Wernher von Braun, Colonel James P. Hamill, U.S.A. (Ret.), Lt. Colonel Robert Staver, A.U.S. (Ret.), and Dr. Walter Dornberger. All of these busy men granted me personal interviews and in many cases made available to me for examination personal papers, photographs, and documents that have never been previously used as source material for a magazine article or a book.

The knowledge of Stanley Crane of the Pequot Library, Southport, Connecticut, that there was a serious void in the literature of World War II and rocketry led to the eventual undertaking of this project. It was completed thanks to the support of W. Clement Stone, President of the Combined Insurance Company of America. The encouragement of writers is but one of the myriad and varied interests of Clem Stone, a writer himself. During its writing I have benefited from the constructive editorial guidance of Oliver Swan and Lawrence Hughes, to whom I owe a special debt.

J. McG.

# NOTES AND SOURCES

This book is neither a technical discussion nor a history of rocketry. Therefore I have not included a bibliography of books in these areas. An excellent and extensive one, however, is available in *Aeronautics and Astronautics. An American Chronology of Science and Technology in the Exploration of Space* (Washington, 1961), by Eugene M. Emme, Historian of the National Aeronautics and Space Administration. In my opinion, the most readable single volume on the history of rocketry, with technical aspects presented in an understandable fashion, available to the general reader is Willy Ley's *Rockets, Missiles, and Space Travel* (New York, revised edition 1959). However, an indication of the principal sources upon which I drew for the background material in this book is in order. Mingled with these citations will be found additional information on each chapter which may be of interest. Out of all the many interviews, reminiscences, published sources, documents, and correspondence, contradictions inevitably arose. I believe that I have collated these sources and given an accurate account of what transpired. In any case, none of the organizations or individuals who provided me with indispensable help is to be regarded as endorsing either the facts or the conclusions in this book. This responsibility is mine alone.

CHAPTER ONE
    For the description of the hiding of the V-2 documents, I have drawn on Chapter 13 of *Peenemünde to Canaveral* (Englewood Cliffs, N. J.), by Dieter K. Huzel, one of the participants. A de-

tailed account of the Sandys investigation is given in Chapter 4 of *Rocket* (London, 1957), by Air Chief Marshal Philip Joubert de la Ferté. Constance Babington-Smith's experiences in photo interpretation are related in her *Air Spy* (New York, 1957). Sir Winston Churchill has described his part in the V-weapon investigations in the thirteenth chapter of *Closing the Ring* (Boston, 1951), the fifth volume of his series *The Second World War*. The early development of the V-weapons and the British-American operations against them are recorded in *History of German Missiles: Hitler's Secret Weapon—Facts and Dreams* (Foreign Documents Evaluation Branch, Aberdeen Proving Ground, Maryland, 1946) and *MI 4/14, The German Long Range Rocket Programme: 1930-1945* (G-2 Document Library, the Pentagon).

## CHAPTER TWO

The experiences of Wernher von Braun and Walter Dornberger are based on my interviews with both men and on the latter's book, *V2: Der Schuss ins Weltall* (Esslingen, 1952). Translated into English by James Cleugh and Geoffrey Halliday, this book was published in London and New York in 1954 as *V-2*. It has a value beyond its interesting technical descriptions of rocket development in the candid, and often startling, insights it gives into the political jockeying and personal rivalries surrounding the German rocket program. For the account of the British attack on Peenemünde, I have drawn on *Bomber Offensive* (London, 1946), by Marshal of the Royal Air Force Sir Arthur Harris, and especially upon the post-raid interrogations of Wing Commander Searby and the other participants, which are printed in detail in Chapter 5 of Joubert de la Ferté's *Rocket, op. cit.*

## CHAPTER THREE

1. Winston S. Churchill, *The Second World War*, Vol. 5, *Closing the Ring* (Boston, 1951), pp. 235-236.

2. *Ibid.*, pp.236-237.

3. *Ibid.*, p. 238.

4. *The Army Air Forces in World War II*, Vol. 3., *Europe: Argument to V-E Day* (Chicago, 1951), p. 85.

5. Wernher von Braun's father, Baron Magnus von Braun, who had been Minister of Agriculture in the Papen cabinet that immediately preceded Hitler's coming to power in January 1933,

liked to recall that a von Braun had fought the Mongols at Lieg-
nitz in 1242. Baron von Braun stayed out of politics after 1933.
His autobiography, *Von Ostpressussen bis Texas* (Stollhamm/
Oldenberg, 1955), contains some interesting material about the
von Braun family and his emigration to the United States to join
his two sons. Wernher von Braun joined the Army rocket program in 1932. Though awarded an Iron Cross and a titular pro-
fessorship for his technical services to the Third Reich, he did
not join the Nazi party until 1942. This lack of political interest,
shared by most of the engineers at Peenemünde, must have frustrated Himmler; it was difficult to prove that men were traitors
or security risks when they ignored politics and concentrated on
their technical specialties.

    6. *The Army Air Forces in World War II, op. cit.*, p. 106

    For this chapter I have also drawn on Babington-Smith, *op.
cit.; Overture to Overlord* (New York, 1950), by Lieutenant General Sir Frederick Morgan; *The Brereton Diaries* (New York,
1946), by Lieutenant General Lewis H. Brereton; *Alsos* (New
York, 1947), by Dr. Samuel A. Goudsmit. As for the *Crossbow*
Committee, this was presided over by Winston Churchill and
consisted of high-ranking British officers, principally from the
Royal Air Force, assisted by scientific advisers from the universities and private industry. On December 29, 1943, Secretary of
War Stimson formed an American *Crossbow* Committee under
the chairmanship of Major General Stephen G. Henry, Director
of the War Department New Developments Division. Later, representatives of the various branches of the American armed services, assisted by American scientists, were attached to an overall
British-American *Crossbow* Committee. The British representation, however, remained dominant. The scope of *Crossbow*, whose
purpose was unknown to anyone but the members of the committee and Allied military and government leaders who numbered
fewer than one hundred, can be summarized with one statistic
among many: over four million prints were developed from aerial
photographs of the suspected sites in northern France. There are
two accounts of *Crossbow* available to the general reader. One
is contained in Chapters 12, 13, 14, and 15 of the British official
history *The Defence of the United Kingdom* (H.M. Stationery
Office, London, 1957) by Basil Collier, from which I have drawn
for many of the facts in this and other chapters. The other is in
the third volume of the seven-volume U.S. official history, *The*

*Army Air Forces in World War II, op. cit.,* Chapter 5, "Crossbow," and Chapter 15, "Crossbow—Second Phase," both written by Joseph W. Angell. Other sources for *Crossbow* were the following reports issued by the United States Strategic Bombing Survey: *Military Analysis Division. Crossbow Campaign* (Washington, 1945); *Report on the Crossbow Campaign: The Air Offensive Against the V Weapons* (Washington, 1945); and *Aircraft Industry Report* (Washington, 1947).

Von Braun has written of his experiences with Himmler, and at the test site in Poland in Chapter 1, "From Small Beginnings," of the book *Project Satellite* (New York, 1958), edited by Kenneth Gatland.

CHAPTER FOUR

1. Dwight D. Eisenhower, *Crusade in Europe* (Garden City, N. Y., 1948), p. 239.

2. *The Army Air Forces in World War II, op. cit.,* p. 527.

3. Eisenhower, *op. cit.,* p. 260.

4. The last V-1 to reach England was shot down on March 29, 1945. In all, 8,000 V-1's were launched against England; 2,400 got through, killing 5,865 people, causing 17,197 major and 23,174 minor casualties, destroying 24,491 dwellings and rendering 52,293 more uninhabitable. It should be noted, however, that the conventional planes of Bomber Command caused five times more damage in a single night's work against Hamburg. And no objectives of military importance were hit by V-1, according to *Despatch by Air Chief Marshal Sir Roderic Hill, Air Operations by Air Defence of Great Britain and Fighter Command in Connection with the German Flying Bomb and Rocket Offensives, 1944-1945*, London Gazette, No. 38437 (1948). This is a comprehensive report, hereinafter cited as the Hill *Despatch,* on the arrival of the V-weapons and the countermeasures taken against them.

In addition to the Hill *Despatch,* other published sources upon which I drew for this chapter were Lieutenant General Morgan's *Overture to Overlord,* op. cit.; Gordon Harrison's *Cross-Channel Attack* (Washington, Office of the Chief of Military History, 1951); Forrest C. Pogue's *The Supreme Command* (Washington, Office of the Chief of Military History, 1954); Walter Bedell Smith's *Eisenhower's Six Great Decisions: Europe 1944-1945* (New York, 1956); and *Now It Can Be Told: The Story of the Manhattan Project* (New York, 1962), by Lieutenant General

Leslie A. Groves. The latter book, together with Dr. Goudsmit's *Alsos, op. cit.*, contains interesting material bearing on Allied concern over the progress of German atomic bomb development.

## CHAPTER FIVE

1. A more detailed account of the "Swedish Incident" may be found in Vol. 2, No. 9 (September 1944), of *Impact,* a publication now declassified, but classified as confidential at the time of its issuance and circulated to British and U.S. officers by the Office of the Chief of Air Staff, Intelligence, the Pentagon. Although the opportunity to examine the fragments of the V-2 that had broken up over Kalmar was a great breakthrough, "misleading evidence on this point [that the V-2 was guided by remote radio control] led to wasted efforts to forestall, detect, and hamper nonexistent radio transmission . . ." according to Air Chief Marshal Sir Roderic Hill in his *Despatch, op. cit.*

2. Churchill, *op. cit.*, p. 234.

3. Shirley Thomas, *Men of Space,* Vol. 2 (New York and Philadelphia, 1961), p. 29. The chapter on Thomas Dixon in this volume gives an interesting account of the typical experiences of American technical investigators in Europe in World War II. As of April 1964, Dixon was Deputy Associate Administrator of the National Aeronautics and Space Administration.

4. Winston S. Churchill, *The Second World War,* Vol. 6, *Triumph and Tragedy* (Boston, 1953), p. 50.

The experiences of von Braun and Dornberger as related in this chapter are based on interviews, as well as Dornberger's *V-2, op. cit.*, and von Braun's writing in *Project Satellite, op. cit.* For the description of the activities of the Polish Underground in this and earlier chapters, I have drawn upon two principal sources: *Destiny Can Wait: The Polish Air Force in the Second World War* (London, 1949), edited by M. Lisiewicz, translated from the Polish by A. Truscoe, and *The Unseen and Silent: Adventures from the Underground Movement Narrated by Paratroops of the Polish Home Army* (London, 1954), translated from the Polish by George Iranek-Osmecki.

## CHAPTER SIX

1. Construction of the tunnels of the *Mittelwerke* was begun in 1936 by a private company which later used them for storing gasoline and mineral oils. The existing facilities were taken over

and expanded by the SS after the August 17, 1943, air raid on Peenemünde. A detailed description of the *Mittelwerke* is contained in the *Aircraft Industry Report* (Washington, 1947) of the United States Strategic Bombing Survey.

2. One hundred and fifty copies of the *A-4 Fibel* were printed and distributed to German field units in an attempt to bridge the gap between formidable laboratory reports and the level of expertise of the average soldier assigned to fire the rocket. One of the primers, now something of a collector's item, was edited by John Bitner, translated by Specialist Ted Woerner, and published in 1957 by the Reports Publications Section, Development Operations Division, Army Ballistics Missile Agency, Redstone Arsenal, Huntsville, Alabama.

3. William L. Shirer, *The Rise and Fall of the Third Reich* (New York, 1960), p. 1040.

4. The complete text of Duncan Sandys' press statement was printed in *The Times* of September 8, 1944.

5. My facts here are drawn from the authoritative Hill *Despatch, op. cit.*

6. A correlation of British and German sources, whose figures vary slightly, indicates that approximately 1,359 V-2's were actually launched against England, of which 1,115 fell on that country or within sight of its shore. Five hundred and eighteen V-2's impacted within the London Civil Defence Region. They had "little, or no, military effect," according to the *Aircraft Industry Report, op. cit.* V-2's killed 2,754 British civilians and seriously injured another 6,523. These casualty figures, much less than those caused by V-1, are appalling enough but can be regarded in historical perspective. The V-2 campaign that produced them lasted seven months. In fourteen hours beginning on the night of February 14, 1945, British and American heavy bombers attacked the city of Dresden. According to Sydney Gruson, writing in the *New York Times* of May 19, 1963, "In the bombing and fires that followed, an estimated total of 135,000 people died. . . . Sixteen hundred acres of Dresden were bombed or burned out, nearly three times the area of London destroyed during the entire war." The Belgian port of Antwerp, captured by Allied forces on September 4, 1944, was actually hit by more V-2's (1,675) than London. The greatest number of rockets to fall on any city in a single day—26—impacted in Antwerp on December 23 and 26, 1944. But 26 rockets, each carrying a ton of high explosives, could not come

close to neutralizing the port of Antwerp, or even to giving effective support to Von Rundstedt's December offensive through the Ardennes. In its objective postwar report, however, the United States Strategic Bombing Survey did cautiously note: "Had the Germans started the V-2 campaign a year before the actual use and with 10 times the quantity involved, the story . . . might have been considerably different, as there were no known counter measures, except the bombing of the launching devices . . . small, portable, and easily camouflaged."

7. Hilary St. George Saunders, *Royal Air Force 1939-1945*, Vol. III, *The Fight Is Won* (London, 1954), p. 174. Official histories can often be tedious going. This one is not. I have drawn upon it for many of the facts in this chapter and also for the author's side comments on the reactions of Londoners to the V-2 bombardment. These are illuminating on the human level as, for example, when he notes on p. 175 that women were more affected than men by V-2, "for many of them the fear of injury from flying glass was very real. . . ."

8. This episode is noted in David Dallin's *Soviet Espionage* (New Haven, 1955), p. 268.


CHAPTER SEVEN

1. Shirer, *op. cit.,* p. 1097.

2. Huzel, *op. cit.,* p. 119.

3. Willy Ley, *Rockets, Missiles, and Space Travel* (New York, rev. ed., 1959), p. 243.

A good part of this chapter is based on interviews with von Braun and Dornberger.

4. Based on a letter report, dated March 9, 1945, written by Staver in London and sent to Trichel in Washington. A copy of this report was made available to me by Staver.


CHAPTER EIGHT

1. The Alsos mission, organized by Lieutenant General Leslie Groves, head of the Manhattan Project, and led in Europe by Dr. Samuel Goudsmit, professor of physics at Northwestern University, did not learn for certain that the Germans had failed to separate Uranium 235 and would have no atom bomb in World War II until U.S. troops occupied Strasbourg in mid-November 1944. At the university there, Dr. Goudsmit found some personal

letters exchanged by leading German physicists that indicated to his trained eye that the German atom bomb effort had failed. By V-E day, the leading German nuclear physicists had been rounded up and sent to Farm Hall, a country estate in England, for interrogation. It was there, on August 6, 1945, that the Germans learned that the Americans had dropped an atom bomb on Hiroshima. The German nuclear physicists were eventually returned to Germany. Unlike the men who had developed the long-range rocket, they had nothing of real value to offer the Allies. This story is told in the interesting but little-known book by Dr. Goudsmit, *Alsos, op. cit.,* and in Lieutenant General Groves's *Now It Can Be Told: The Story of the Manhattan Project, op. cit.*

2. The complete story of Hermes is detailed in *Final Report, Project Hermes, V-2 Missile Program,* General Electric Report No. R52 AO510, September 1952, and U. S. Army, Ordnance, *Hermes Guided Missile Research and Development Project, 1944-1954* (Washington, 1959).

This chapter is also based on interviews with Staver and Toftoy and documents supplied by both men.


CHAPTER NINE

1. Shirer, *op. cit.,* p. 1104. For background material about Hitler and the German conduct of the war in general, I have drawn upon Shirer and Alan Bullock's *Hitler: A Study in Tyranny* (New York, 1952).

Most of this chapter is based on von Braun and Dornberger interviews, the latter's *V-2, op. cit.,* and Huzel's *Peenemünde to Canaveral, op. cit.*


CHAPTER TEN

1. Robert Staver provided the author with an exact copy of the complete text of this CIOS Target Data Sheet.

2. This Intelligence Summary for March 11, 1945, of the Supreme Headquarters, Allied Expeditionary Forces, is quoted by Chester Wilmot in his *Struggle for Europe* (New York, 1952), p. 690.

3. This quotation is taken from *History of Army Air Forces Participation in Project Paperclip, 1945-1947,* compiled by Edna Jensen and Harriet Buyer and issued in August 1948 by the Re-

search Studies Institute of the Air University, Maxwell Air Force Base, Alabama, with the classification of Secret. This is a formidable four-volume work covering the entire project in all its phases. It contains contemporary interviews, official orders, cables, and memoranda, and I have drawn on it heavily for documentary support in this book. Its classification has now been downgraded from Secret to Restricted and it is available for examination to anyone with a legitimate interest in *Overcast* and *Paperclip*. It was made available to me from the excellent archives of the Research Studies Institute through the courtesy of Lieutenant Colonel Gene Guerney, Director of the United States Air Force Book Program, and Mr. Albert Simpson, USAF Historian.

4. Soviet claims for reparations are discussed in detail in General Lucius D. Clay's *Decision in Germany* (New York, 1950).

5. In addition to Dr. Porter, the General Electric engineers on the Project Hermes team were Dr. R. H. Norris, Dr. A. Liebhafsky, Ed Hull, and Walt Hausz. The guided-missile targets these men had to investigate were by no means restricted to Nordhausen and the V-2. The Germans had also developed a series of revolutionary anti-aircraft missiles called *Taifun* (Typhoon), *Schmetterling* (Butterfly), *Enzian* (Gentian), *Rheintochter* (Rhine Maiden), *Wasserfall* (Waterfall), as well as a method for firing rockets from submerged submarines which presaged the Polaris of today. Research on these devices, as well as on V-2, was done not only at Peenemünde and Nordhausen-Bleicherode but at outside support organizations, such as universities, from one end of Germany to the other. Dr. Porter, for example, spent a busy April 1945 in West Germany tracking down and interrogating scores of professors and technicians at the University of Heidelberg and the Darmstadt *Technische Hochschule*.

Other background material for this chapter has been derived from Staver, Porter, and Toftoy interviews. For the capture of Nordhausen by U.S. combat units, I have consulted: *Spearhead in the West, 1941-1945: The Third Armored Division*. (Frankfurt am/Main/Schwanheim, 1945); *A History of the Third Armored Division (Spearhead), April 1941-July 1958* (Darmstadt, 1958); and *Timberwolf Tracks: The History of the 104th Infantry Division, 1942-1945* (Washington, 1946). Although they make for somewhat grim reading, the personal experiences of some of the inmates of the Dora and Nordhausen concentration camps are recorded in

*Mémorial des Camps de Dora-Ellrich* (Paris, 1949), and Henri Arvet's *Des Geôles de la Gestapo de Dijon à L'Enfer de Buchenwald et Dora* (Dijon, 1948).

### CHAPTER ELEVEN

1. Dornberger, *V-2* (British Edition), *op. cit.,* p. 254.

2. Fritz Zwicky, *Report on Certain Phases of War Research in Germany,* dated October 1, 1945, p. 173. This report is in the archives of the Air Force Museum, Wright-Patterson Air Force Base, Dayton, Ohio.

3. The source of these predictions of von Braun's and those of Dornberger that follow was *The Story of Peenemünde, or What Might Have Been: Peenemünde East Through the Eyes of 500 Detained at Garmisch.* This is a 729-page document compiled in 1945 by various research people attached to the then Army Air Forces and was made available to me from the archives of the Research Studies Institute of the Air University, Maxwell Air Force Base, Alabama, through the courtesy of Lieutenant Colonel Gene Guerney and Mr. Albert Simpson. This document offers a complete record of the activities, life histories, and technical interrogations of the key German rocket personnel. The interrogations at Garmisch were conducted by CIOS Team No. 183, headed by Lieutenant Colonel John O'Mara of the Army Air Forces Engineering Division at Wright Field, Ohio. British interests were represented by Squadron Leaders B. A. Sharpe and E. G. Kenney, Flight Lieutenants R. H. Block and H. R. Stokes, and Major J. Iball and Lieutenant Colonel C. J. Gollin of the Ministry of Supply. Fritz Zwicky was the principal interrogator for the U. S. Army Air Forces. The U. S. Navy Technical Intelligence Mission was represented by Lieutenant (j.g.) P. H. Wilkinson, Carl H. Smith, Dr. Ernst Krause from the Naval Research Laboratory in Washington, and Dr. Clark Millikan, director of the Guggenheim Aeronautical Laboratory at the California Institute of Technology. Dr. Richard Porter and his General Electric Project Hermes team represented the interests of U. S. Army Ordnance. From a reading of this document, upon which I have drawn heavily for many of the facts in this book, it is apparent that Porter conducted the bulk of the more rewarding interrogations.

For military operations described in this chapter, I have consulted General Jean de Lattre de Tassigny's *History of the First French Army* (London, 1952, translated from the French by Malcolm Barnes); *The Seventh United States Army in France and Germany 1944-1945; Report of Operations* (Heidelberg, 1946); *Combat History of the 44th Infantry Division* (Atlanta, 1946); and *Combat History of the 324th Infantry Regiment, 44th Infantry Division* (Baton Rouge, 1946).

There is no documentation for the experiences of Dornberger and von Braun at Oberjoch. Here I have had to draw upon interviews with both men.

## CHAPTER TWELVE

1. *Foreign Relations of the United States. Diplomatic Papers. The Conferences at Malta and Yalta, 1945.* (Washington, 1955), p. 114. The documents prepared by the European Advisory Commission were formally signed and issued in Berlin on June 5, 1945. For a fuller discussion of this matter, see Lucius D. Clay's *Decision in Germany, op. cit.,* pp. 13-17.

2. Much of this chapter is based on conversations with Hamill, Toftoy, Bromley, and correspondence with Holmes. Most of my facts have been drawn from a report dated June 7, 1945, subject: Evacuation of V-2 Missiles from Nordhausen, Germany, written by Major Bromley and filed with Colonel Toftoy. According to this report, Bromley acted "in compliance with verbal instructions from Colonel H. N. Toftoy, and with the authority of secret-priority cable from Supreme Headquarters, 12th Army Group." Bromley was awarded a Bronze Star for this operation. As of June 1964, he was a colonel stationed at the Pentagon.

## CHAPTER THIRTEEN

1. A copy of this cable was made available to me by Robert Staver. A copy of it is also one of the many documents included in *History of AAF Participation in Project Paperclip, op. cit.*

For the story of the location and evacuation of the V-2 documents, I have drawn upon a lengthy letter report, dated May 23, 1946, from Staver to Colonel S. B. Ritchie of the Research and Development Service, Office Chief of Ordnance, the Pentagon.

## CHAPTER FOURTEEN

1. Churchill, *Triumph and Tragedy,* op. cit., p. 605. I have also read President Truman's *Memoirs,* Vol. I, *Year of Decisions* (New York, 1955).

2. *Documents of German History* (New Brunswick, N. J., 1958),

edited by Louis Snyder, p. 472. For a fuller discussion of JCS/1067, see General Clay's *Decision in Germany, op. cit.*

This chapter is also based on Porter and Staver interviews and documents supplied by both men.

CHAPTER FIFTEEN

1. *Red Star in Space* (New York, 1963), by Martin Caidin, is an interesting popular history of Russian rocket development.

2. This entire conversation is recorded in *History of AAF Participation in Project Paperclip, op. cit.*

3. *Ibid.* I have drawn extensively on the documents compiled in *History of AAF Participation in Project Paperclip* in writing this chapter.

4, 5, 6. Copies of these reports were made available to me by Robert Staver.

This chapter is also based on Porter, Staver, Toftoy, von Braun, and Dornberger interviews and background documents supplied by these men.

CHAPTER SIXTEEN

1. From a speech given by Hamill on October 20, 1961, at the tenth annual awards dinner of the American Rocket Society in Huntsville, Alabama, at which von Braun and Toftoy were presented with the Hermann Oberth Award. This dinner was attended by most of the Germans who came to the United States under *Overcast*. In his speech to this group, who form a loose association styled the "Fort Bliss Old Timers," Hamill reviewed at length his experiences at Fort Strong and later at Fort Bliss. Hamill made a copy of this speech available to me, granted me interviews, and provided me with other documents upon which I have drawn for this and other chapters.

Chapters 11, 12, and 13 of *From Hiroshima to the Moon* (New York, 1959), by Daniel Lang contain interesting material about the early experiences of the German group in the United States.

This chapter is also based on Toftoy, von Braun, and Dornberger interviews and *Marshall Space Flight Center Historical Monograph No. 1: Historical Origins of the George C. Marshall Space Flight Center* (Historical Office, Office of Management Services, George C. Marshall Space Flight Center, Huntsville, Alabama, 1960), by David S. Akens, MSFC Historian.

CHAPTER SEVENTEEN

1. There were reasons for the Soviet delay. In the fury of battle, Soviet assault troops had wantonly wrecked many valuable German installations. Then the agents of Malenkov's Special Committee proved too zealous in fulfilling Stalin's Yalta demand for ten billion dollars' worth of technical reparations. Before adequate plans had been made for absorbing them in war-ravaged Russia, whole factories were carted off, only to wind up rusting uselessly on railroad sidings. A stop was put to this practice. Plants were left where they were, and East Germany was combed for specialists to operate them, with the Russians observing and taking notes. By the fall of 1946, conditions in the Soviet Union had improved over the immediate postwar months and Russian technicians had a clearer idea of the ramifications of the German equipment. It is probable that the Soviet action of October 22, 1946, was hastened by an American demand at the Paris Council of Foreign Ministers in July 1946 for a quadripartite investigation of all the occupation zones of Germany to determine whether war munitions were being produced in any of them. In January 1947, a team acting on behalf of the Allied Control Commission investigated the Soviet Zone and was able to report that there were no plants there producing war materials or engaged in military research. By that time, of course, the plants had been dismantled and shipped to the Soviet Union. This whole question is gone into at length in General Clay's *Decision in Germany, op. cit.*

There is very little source material available on the deportation of the German specialists to the Soviet Union, their activities there, and their eventual return to Germany. For portions of this chapter, I have drawn on my own experiences as an intelligence officer of the U. S. Government in postwar Germany. For the Gröttrups' experiences I have drawn on my conversations with them upon their return to West Germany, Frau Gröttrup's diary, published as a book *Die Besessenen und die Machtigen: Im Schatten der Roten Rakete* (*The Possessed and the Powerful: In the Shadows of the Red Rocket* (Stuttgart, 1958), and Helmut Gröttrup: *Aus den Arbeiten des Deutschen Raketen-Kollektive in der Sowjet-Union* (Raketentechnik und Ramfahrtforschung, Heft 2, April 1958). The general reader can consult the following publications:

Kilmarx, Robert A., *A History of Soviet Air Power* (London, 1962), in particular the subsection "Exploitation of German Science and Technology in the Soviet Union" of Chapter 5.

Lee, Asher, editor, *The Soviet Air and Rocket Forces* (New York, 1959), in particular Chapter 9, "Soviet Missiles," by Asher Lee and Richard Stockwell, and Chapter 15, "The German Legacy," by Richard Stockwell.

Parry, Dr. Albert, *Russia's Rockets and Missiles* (New York, 1960), in particular Chapter 8, "The German Role in Russian Rockets."

Schroder, G. W., "How Russian Engineering Looked to a Captured German Scientist," *Aviation Week*, May 9, 1945.

Sokolov, V. L., *Soviet Use of German Science and Technology, 1945-1946* (Research Program of the USSR, New York, 1955).

Zaehringer, Alfred J., *Soviet Space Technology* (New York, 1961), in particular Chapter 2, *Cornerstones.*

CHAPTER EIGHTEEN
   1. Richard Witkin, editor, *The Challenge of the Sputniks* (New York, 1958), p. 4.
   2. Quoted by Parry, *op. cit.*, p. 111.
   For background material in this chapter I have also drawn on *Behind the Sputniks: A Survey of Soviet Space Science* (Washington, 1958); *Inquiry into Satellite and Missile Programs: Hearings Before the Preparedness Investigating Subcommittee of the Committee on Armed Services, United States Senate, 85th Congress* (Washington, U. S. Government Printing Office, 1958); *The Next Ten Years in Space: 1959-1969,* Staff Report of the Select Committee on Astronautics and Space Exploration, House Document No. 115 (Washington, U.S.G.P.O.), 1959; *Historical Origins of the George C. Marshall Space Flight Center, op. cit.,* and documents on the Saturn program provided by the Office of Information, MSFC, during my visit to Huntsville, Alabama.

APPENDIX: SOME QUESTIONS AND FACTS ABOUT OVERCAST/PAPERCLIP
   The facts presented here are drawn principally from the documents in *History of AAF Participation in Project Paperclip, op. cit.,* and *Paperclip: Part I* (Office of Naval Intelligence Review, Washington, 1946).

# INDEX